Table of Contents

Intro

The quest for me to understand the conditions of my race in society and African American history befell on me early in life. I was exposed to racism for the first time at the tender age of five. During the winter of 1994, my father and I attended a football game at Louisiana State University in Baton Rouge, Louisiana. Our seats were on the fourth row near the fifty yard line. Shortly after we made it to our seats, a Caucasian male aggressively tapped my father on his shoulder and bumped the back of my head in the process. The astonishment of him touching my father in such an aggressive manner made me temporarily forget that he bumped my head with no apology. In a reprimanding manner, the male who tapped my father said to him, "Hey boy! Those seats are for the Weinberg family. What the hell are you two doing sitting in them?" My father looked at me, then took a deep breath and smoke from the cold air exhaled through his nose. I became nervous of what he would do next.

My father responded, "I do construction work for their family. They gave me the tickets because they couldn't make it tonight." In disbelief, the man shouted bullshit and demanded to see our tickets. After my father refused, the inquiring male proceeded to walk off in search of security. The security guard scurried to our seats as if he were tending to a fight. Once the guard made it to our seats he told my father, "We need to see yall's ticket stubs." The top flight security guard referred to the inquiring paying customer as a we, as if the other patron was a colleague on his security team. My father responded, "I will show you our tickets, but not another paying customer our tickets." The security guard was apparently on a remedial reading level because it took him an extended amount of time to verify the information on our tickets. Once my father proved that we were in our correct seats, both of the European American males carried on with their nights unapologetically. Others who sat in earshot just watched as we sat embarrassed and did not bother to interject during the harassment. During the altercation I wondered why my father and I were vilified. After examining our surroundings I only noticed one difference between us and others who weren't harassed, skin color.

My next encounter with racism differed greatly from my first one. I attended a predominantly black school each year until fifth grade. The school I attended for fifth grade had a student body that consisted of 95% European Americans. My personality has always been an outgoing one to say the least; however not many words were spoken by me during my first year at the new school. I was in complete culture shock. The culture shock had nothing to do with the financial differences between the other students and myself. The culture shock was existent because most of the teachers and students alienated me due to my differences. Throughout the first year I was often stared at by students because of my different dialect, style, and appearance. Teachers also made the differences evident. Going into my sixth grade year I vowed to remove myself from my shell.

Once I began to open up, students became comfortable making black jokes, poor jokes, and mimicked my urban dialect. Teachers were aware of the foul jokes, but remained silent bystanders.

One day during a history class my sixth grade year, a student made a derogatory statement about people who were on food stamps. Not only was my household utilizing food stamps at the time, but many others who I knew, loved, and respected did also. My classmate's display of ignorance provoked me to admonish her. The teacher chastised me in front of everyone, but told the racist student nothing. Later that same night, my history teacher called my parents to scold my behavior. Throughout the rest of that year, my history teacher echoed white supremacist views, consistently spoke to me in a condescending tone, and used our cultural differences against me. Before the Thanksgiving break that year, she advised my parents that I needed medication to help me learn better and control my behavior. The one day I took the medication that was recommended to me by a person with no medicinal training was the worst day of my life. I was tranquilized from the medication and it did nothing to enhance my learning abilities. The only person who benefited from me ingesting the drug was my history teacher because she didn't have to hear a peep from me that day. Although I only took the pill one day, it had a lasting effect during my years of schooling. Once I fell out of favor with my sixth grade history teacher, word got out that I was a problem child. It did not take long for the word to spread throughout a school that had an average of fifty students per grade ranging from kindergarten to 12th grade. My falsified reputation preceded itself with other teachers who shared my sixth grade history teacher's mindset and they treated me the same way that she did. The time I spent at that school was detrimental to my academic confidence. My grades fell from excellent to mediocre throughout my middle school years.

I enrolled in a predominantly black school for my freshman year of high school. The mixture of my subpar academic confidence and happiness to be in a non-racist environment caused my grades to dip even lower. I felt academically inferior to my other classmates who achieved good grades. Throughout my ninth grade year I remained in the principal's office, detention, and at the bottom academically. My love for writing was discovered during my sophomore year in high school. My English teacher pulled me to the side after she returned our second test of the school year and complimented my writing. At the time I felt it was only a nice gesture because of her sweet personality. Her compliments brought awareness to my abilities, but left me unmotivated to do better in school. After my first round of progress reports that year, my basketball coach told me that I would become ineligible to continue playing if I didn't improve my grades. That threat motivated me to increase my grades to the minimum I needed to remain eligible, but not to excel. My English teacher and I shared a big sense of humor and I loved her positive energy, so we established a great rapport. Her class was the only one during my sophomore year that I looked forward to attending.

My English teacher did not return after the Christmas break that year. She suddenly passed away a day before Christmas. I was distraught when I got the news of her passing. Her replacement was Leonard Williams, the only African American male teacher that I had during my entire eighteen years of schooling. I acted rebellious during his first few weeks of taking over the English class. On the first test he administered, I aced the essay and got almost every question in the other sections wrong. After he returned the test he pulled me aside to question me about how I could do so well on the writing section, but so poorly on the sections that required effort. Prior to that, my poor academic performance was received in acceptance by previous teachers. Mr. Williams viewed it as underachievement and disappointment. He saw me as a resemblance of him and went significantly further than any other teacher to provoke me to utilize my untapped potential. Towards the end of that school year I mailed him a hand written letter of appreciation for the impact he had on my life and academic career. His mentorship resurrected my academic confidence and performance. It also propelled me to obtain a Sociology degree from Tulane University to better understand the development and structures of society and to have an impact on as many others as possible, such as the one he had on me.

Not many young black males will have the opportunity to have a teacher of their same race and gender. Studies unanimously prove that students learn better when they are taught by teachers of their own race and gender. Black males only account for 2% of teachers in the public school system in the United States. My second experience with racism was more detrimental than my first one. A man who harassed my father and I for one night was no comparison to the systematic racism that I experienced. Public schools that I attended were run down, insect infested, offered limited resources, and were inferior in almost every aspect to the private school I attended. The kids who I attended private school with were born with a huge head start and the schooling they received furthered it. Most of the kids that I attended public school with were born into the world disadvantaged and school often pushed them further back. A parent's finances more than often determines what type of education their children will receive. The school system is often overlooked as one of the most effective forms of systematic racism that upholds black oppression and economic racial supremacy. The appropriation of contributions that people of African descent made to civilization in history books and wealth distribution between black and white schools are only a meniscal amount of the ways that the school system upholds racial dominance.

"Crabs In A Barrel" is a popular phrase commonly used to describe a primary obstacle for the black race. The barrel will remain full if it continues to be examined in its original context. The structure of the barrel that has placed the crabs next to each other is more important to evaluate than the next crab. This text proceeds two short stories based on two young black males whose experiences with individuals and structures echoes the sentiment of my different analysis of the phrase, "Crabs In A Barrel".

Barrel In The Streets Part 1

I finally arrived at a fork in the bumpy road of life that I had been traveling on for twenty-five years. As I sat in the living room of my girlfriend's place, I thought about the vital decisions I would have to make if I wanted to take our relationship to the next level. Nicki and I moved in together six months into our relationship. Ten months later, we brought a set of beautiful twin girls into the world. After we had our twin girls, things changed for us financially. When we had no kids and combined both of our minimum wage incomes we were broke, but able to keep the lights on and food in the fridge. Once we brought two children into the household at the same time, we didn't even have enough money to be broke. Improvising was our way of life. During winters we let the oven door down to warm our apartment and used candles at night through all seasons to keep the house lit because we rarely had enough money to keep the lights on. Nicki's sister previously experienced similar hardships until Leroy, her child's father, went to jail. Once Leroy who was also like a big brother to me and one of my closest friends wasn't in the household anymore, she became eligible for all types of government assistance. We decided that I should move in with my mother who lived in the same projects as us, so Nicki could receive those same benefits. Shortly after I moved out, she qualified for a large amount of food stamps, cheaper rent, welfare, and our kids got free daycare. It burned my insides that my family was rewarded by the government for not having me in the household. I couldn't go any longer without being married to the love of my life and not being under the same roof as my kids.

It was part of my morning routine to stop by my family's apartment for breakfast. After I gathered my belongings to leave for the day, I wrapped my arms around Nicki while she was cleaning the dishes then said, "Baby, I don't care if we get dropped from government assistance. I want to move back in and marry you." She put the sponge and bowl back into the soapy sink, then turned towards me and said, "We are going to lose daycare, food stamps, and welfare. I love you Jamal, but uhh no." Our defeated eyes locked, then we hugged each other as she held back tears. After we held each other for about thirty seconds, I made my way towards the front door. It took three steps to get there. When I made it to the threshold I sunk my head into her chest, then she gave me a kiss on the forehead and said, "It's going to be ok baby. We aren't going to be stuck in these projects forever." I wanted to believe her, but we had two children, only one of us had a high school diploma, and both of us worked at fast-food restaurants. Living in the hood felt like a permanent destination.

Leroy who had just came home from jail was sitting on Nicki's porch waiting for me. Before I could cross the threshold and step into the cold winter air he said, "Damn bruh, y'all are a real life soap opera. I don't even see why you want to marry that little girl." Leroy was from the Williamsburg projects. The Williamsburg was in our rival neighborhood on the other side of town. I resided in the St.

Gabriel projects since the age of four when my parents parted ways. Leroy moved to the St. Gabriel after half of the Williamsburg shut down when we were still teenagers. Before the city closed down several projects and shipped the residents to rival neighborhoods, violence was trending downwards throughout the city. Once people were displaced into rival neighborhoods, an explosion of violence occurred and our city was deemed as the murder capital. It may sound strange, but I actually felt safe in the projects before our rival hood moved in. Previous to that, everyone knew and respected each other's role in the hood. The elderly were left alone and the youth who were into sports and extracurricular activities were not influenced by older people that were doing wrong. Most of the violence that previously occurred were targeted crimes against others who were into that life. When the rival project moved in, saying all hell broke loose would be an understatement. The number of people who moved in from the Williamsburg was not an overwhelming amount, but the ones who did move had an overwhelming amount of motivation to be feared and respected. Elderly, kids, and law abiding citizens were no longer safe. They would be robbed, jumped, and sometimes victims of deadly crossfire. Almost everyone from the Williamsburg became a target because of the disruption. Leroy was an exception. His Uncle Gee was one of the biggest drug dealers in the St. Gabriel and the neighborhood hero. I called him Uncle Gee also. Once Leroy's father was killed at the age of six, he split time between the two projects because his mother wanted him to have a male figure in his life. Splitting time in the St. Gabriel was how he met Nicki's sister. She was the trophy girl in the projects. Guys would have fights over her and didn't even have her phone number. Nicki's sister and Leroy became an item when they were fourteen years old, but things changed on Leroy's eighteenth birthday.

Part 2

Uncle Gee wanted to go all out to celebrate Leroy's eighteenth birthday. He loved Leroy more than he loved himself. I remember that summer day years ago, as if it were today. On June 22, 1988, as soon as the sun began to fall into the evening sky, Leroy sat propped up on the backseat of a royal blue drop top Corvette while being chauffeured by Uncle Gee's driver down the main street in the middle of the St. Gabriel projects. His driver's name was Tony. Tony was a middle aged Italian man that had slicked back jet black hair and was the size of a retired professional football lineman. Uncle Gee rode in the passenger's seat and shouted through a megaphone for most of the ride. I sat in the backseat behind him next to Leroy. A second line band trailed us as we cruised through the projects. His birthday parade could have made the prince of England and championship professional sports teams jealous. Once we finished cruising through the St. Gabriel, the party did not stop there. We traveled uptown to the Williamsburg to do the same thing. I felt like Simi in the movie "Coming To America". Many people enjoyed the parade, but it intensified the hate of some people who disliked Uncle Gee. Everyone loved him, besides the people that wanted to be him. Throughout the second trip I grew paranoid of our safety. I remained calm for the rest of the ride while Tony silently drove with two hands on the wheel.

After the parade wrapped up, we stopped a block around the corner from the Williamsburg at Leroy's aunt's house. I went inside to use the bathroom while everyone was in the house besides Uncle Gee. He stood outside smoking a cigarette by his car. As I washed my hands in the bathroom, I heard Leroy and his aunt in the living room laughing. The bathroom was right next to the front door. If you looked out of the bathroom window, you could see the street. After I dried my hands with the last paper towel left, I heard a flurry of gunshots from machine guns that seemed never ending. I dove on the floor simultaneously as the shots riddled a car near the front of the house. After the shots ceased, I pushed myself off the ground by placing my hands in a cold puddle of tears then scrambled behind the shower curtain incase the beef came inside. Before my shoulder could touch the bottom of the half emptied tub, I heard the screen door slam and a car pull off. It felt like the house was empty, but no matter how clear the coast was I knew it was not safe. I peeked through the crack of the bathroom door and no one was in sight. Because of the loud gunshots that took place, I knew exiting through the front door would eventually place me on a witness stand which I wanted no parts of. Also staying on the scene or calling 911 would put me in the same predicament. After taking a leap of faith, I dashed out the back door. I cleared the back fence as if I were an Olympian hurdler and treated the backstreet as the finish line. When I made it to the street behind Leroy's aunt's house, I began to walk as if nothing happened. My heart pounded so fast, I was surprised that I couldn't see it beating through my shirt. I power walked from one side of the city to the other side and still don't remember anything about that walk besides my thunderous heartbeat.

When I got within two blocks of my place, it hit me that going back home was not the best idea. At that moment I was not sure if Tony, Leroy, or Uncle Gee were a part of the shooting and if any other partakers in the shooting knew me or my whereabouts. To avoid being in a place that I could easily be found, I went to the east side of the city where my father resided. We rarely talked and I hated him so much for not being active in my life. I even disliked myself sometimes because we looked just alike. It gave me the deepest pain to resent a person who looked just like me. My mother's sperm donor lived with his wife and their three kids. His wife was a sweet woman, but I felt like she was the person who took him away from me, so I disliked her and her kids. When I arrived at his doorstep, the look on my face said it all. My plain white t-shirt was loose around the collar, soaked from sweat, and I smelled like zoo dirt. After my father examined me from head to toe, he gave me a hug that I never wanted to end. He then led me to the guest room and pulled out a set of towels and a change of clothes. I was always envious of my younger siblings because they stayed under the same roof with my dad and they lived in a gated community. I always felt like I was on an exotic resort when I was at my dad's house. My youngest siblings were a set of identical twin boys that looked just like their mother and the older brother looked just like my father. After I showered and sat on the edge of the bed in silence, my oldest sibling knocked on the door and called my name. Before I could get up, my father told him to let me rest because I was not feeling good. It felt like I went to sleep before I laid down that night.

The next morning I woke up a few hours later than usual. It felt like no one was in the house, but I wasn't comfortable enough to check. The television in the guest room only had basic channels, so I turned on the news. I usually only watched the news for the sports segment. When I turned on the news the sports segment was just ending and a reporter was briefing the listeners about the 198th murder in the city before the commercial break. I had to use the bathroom, but something kept me in bed until the news returned from commercial break. The crime scene of the 198th murder near the halfway mark of the year was the house that I escaped from. Leroy's aunt's driveway had yellow tape around it and Uncle Gee's car had an uncountable amount of gunshot holes. I just knew that it was him inside of the body bag being rolled away. "The 198th murder in the city, which is a record high, does not have any leads to a motive and the gunmen are still at large. If you have any information please call the Crimesolvers hotline at 555-865-2199", was what I heard in a backdrop voice as the sight of the murder scene chilled my heart.

Uncle Gee was the first person close to me that I lost to gun violence. The fact that he died moments after we last spoke made me realize how delicate life is. After I cried until I got dehydrated, my father crept in the guest room and placed his arm around me. I spent the remainder of that summer living at my father's house. Throughout the summer he took me on trips, taught me life lessons, and showed me a love that I couldn't even dream of. It was as if he were the perfect father besides his absence in my life. My mom didn't give me the option of staying by my father's house once the summer ended. I pried on why I couldn't stay, but she couldn't put together a reasonable reason. My school was closer to my father's house, I would have been in a better neighborhood, and the dust had not settled with the murder yet. My father and I went to dinner together the night before I had to move back in with my mom. My anxiety was through the roof while we were on the way to the restaurant. I knew that would be the best time to ask him why he had been missing for most of my life.

Before the waiter could take our drink orders I asked my dad, "Why have you been gone most of my life?" He looked away, then looked at me and said, "I will tell you when you get older son." My mother never shied away from telling me about him, so I raised my voice and said, "After everything I have been through without you, I deserve an explanation!" Tables in earshot turned and looked our way after my outburst. My dad's eyes progressively watered for about thirty seconds until tears ran on the table, then he broke his silence.

"Son, your momma and I began having problems about two years before you were born. I owe her the respect not to tell you why we had problems, but I do owe you the respect to let you know why I haven't been able to be the father I wanted to be for you. On your fourth birthday your mom asked could we take a break from our relationship. For ten months I stayed committed to her although we weren't together and I spent as much time with you as she would allow me to. I asked your mom could you all accompany me for the weekend of my twentieth year class reunion. She declined and my heart was broken because all of my friends from high school knew about you and wanted to meet you. On the first night of the reunion I was the first person to arrive at the opening event. The second person to arrive was a classmate that I barely remembered from high school, but she was all I remembered from that weekend. Me and her fell in love almost instantly. For the first two months that your stepmom and I dated I still tried to get back with your mother, but she wouldn't budge. I would have dumped her at the drop of a dime to get back with your mom. After about six months we stopped being quiet about our relationship. When your momma got wind of my new love interest, she stopped letting me see you. I didn't want to get the court system involved, but that seemed like my only option. Your mom was granted sole custody and I was supposed to have you every other weekend. I held my end of the deal and paid child support consistently, but she still kept you away from me. I took it back to the courts, but the fight dragged on and they didn't hold her accountable for not letting me see you. When my legal options dried up, I decided to take a different route. I showed up at yall's place on a weekend when I was supposed to come get you, and her ex-boyfriend greeted me at the door with an AK-47 around his neck. A part of me died when I pulled off from your mom's place that day. Although my life was threatened, that was a fight I should have fought until the death of me. I know your mom dragged my name through the mud and ain't no telling what she told you about me, but son I love you so much and wanted to be there every day for you. I stress almost every day because she stopped me from being an intricate part of your life."

My dad's version of the story left me speechless and the rest of our dinner only consisted of a few more words. Only emotions spoke for the remainder of that night. A part of me died when I realized that my mom always had negative things to say about my father and that every time we would try to see each other, she shut it down. The love for my mom was unalterable, but a severe strain was placed on our relationship after all she did was cry when I confronted her about why she didn't allow my father to be a part of my life. I was robbed of a father by my own mother.

Things changed for me in the projects when I moved back home. I went the entire summer without hearing from Leroy. Prior to that summer, I was accustomed to talking to him every day. The only time I saw him that summer was at Uncle Gee's funeral. While my father and I sat parked outside of my mother's place, I spotted Leroy and Tony parked in a car up the street. After I fell into a deep stare watching them, my father gently shook me on my shoulder and asked, "What's wrong son? It looks like you just saw a ghost." I uttered, "No it's all good. I'm just not ready to go back home." I really wasn't ready to go back home, but seeing Leroy and Tony smoking in a car together was the cause for my mood change. I never saw them hang together previous to that sighting. Before I got out of the car my father said, "Things will change going forward son. I will be closer to you than ever." We agreed to sneak and meet up twice a week. Once to walk in the park and once at the library. My dad was over 300 pounds before I moved in with him that summer. He trimmed down to 280 pounds when it was time for me to move back home. His wife always had something negative to say when I talked about working out and eating healthy. I prayed that he didn't revert back to his old habits after I moved out.

Two weeks after I moved back home, my dad died of a massive heart attack. The pain I felt when Uncle Gee died wasn't a fraction of the pain I felt when my father passed away. The man who I hated almost my entire life made me love him during my most vulnerable time. If I didn't spend any time with him that previous summer, I wouldn't have felt any pain when he died and would have skipped his funeral. I always felt my dad didn't even care about my existence and wellbeing. Getting close with him right before his death shattered the cold heart I had left. He was the opposite of what I painted him to be, or better yet, what my mom painted him to be. I went to the funeral with Leroy because I did not feel right going with my father's other family and I definitely did not want to go with my mother. When I saw they were serving the same food that killed my dad at the repast, I left.

My best friend at school dropped out before the prior school year ended. I wanted to quit also after my father died, but I had good grades and that seemed like the only way out of the hood. After he dropped out, I began to hang with a guy named Trent who lived in the St. Gabriel also. We didn't have much of a rapport established, but we caught the same bus together since elementary school, so he was the perfect rebound friend. Trent and I didn't have much in common besides our great grades and where we were from. He was very quiet and picked on often. For the first month of school I did great in every class besides history and math. My math teacher was terrible at explaining how to work through problems. It was as if she was trying to learn geometry, while trying to teach it. Because I was known for being a smart kid, she felt I was supposed to easily pick up on her subject, although she didn't either. I was never fond of United States history, but the teacher made the class even worse. She spoke to everyone in a very condescending tone and acted like it was a burden to be there. That was the class when I would drift off and think about my problems outside of school.

On a Monday during the second month of school, a bully that usually picked on Trent kept messing with him while we ate lunch together in the cafeteria. The bully sat a few seats over from us and kept whispering to Trent that he was a bitch. After the fourth time he whispered to Trent that he was a bitch I asked him, "Who are you talking to?" He looked at me and said, "I was talking to your friend, but now I am talking to you, bitch!" I smiled and responded, "You got it." He said, "I know I got it bitch." The bell signifying the end of lunch rang immediately after he called me a bitch for the second time. History was the next class after lunch and all three of us happened to have that class together.

Trent sat in the front row, just like he did in every other class. I sat on the second row from the back and the bully sat directly behind me. During the first half of class he kept whispering things to me under his breath, but I couldn't make out what he was saying. During the second half of class the teacher did an activity where she would call students to the board to answer a question. Typically, the bully was the only person who participated less than me. That day was the first time he volunteered to do anything in class other than be an asshole. Right after he got up to walk to the chalkboard, he plucked me on the back of my neck. Once he got to the chalkboard he finally got a question right and people started clapping for him because of how intellectually challenged he was. Before he passed me up on the way back to his seat he kicked my right shin. My last nerve was gone with the wind. I immediately got up and punched him in his mouth and he fell on the other row of desks next to us. I jumped over the fallen desks then got on top of him and took all of my built up anger out on his face. It took about four of my classmates to pull me off of him. I could hear the teacher yelling, "Call the police!" as security escorted me to the principal's office.

That pummeling resulted in a five day suspension from school. I spent my first two days of suspension hanging with Leroy. The second day felt like perfect timing to ask Leroy something that I wanted to ask him since the first day I returned home from the summer. While Leroy and I were walking to the corner store I asked him, "Why have you been hanging with Tony?" Leroy looked at me and laughed for a half of block. He erased his laughter then stopped and said, "That man knows the people who killed my uncle. He wants to handle business, but I think he is bluffing. I am going to be able to tell if he is bluffing real soon." The term "handle business" was subjective, but I assumed I knew what it meant from the context clues. I wanted no parts of that conversation, so I left it alone for the rest of the evening. Later that night Leroy asked could he sleep by my place until I returned to school. My mom was still drowning in guilt about the situation with my father, so she didn't object although I was in trouble.

Over the next few days Leroy began to act very strange. Usually he was never short on words, but he seemed dazed and in another world most of the time. I would have to repeat my questions two or three times to get him to respond and he added nothing to our conversations. Leroy didn't even laugh at his favorite television shows. During that entire week we went everywhere together, but that Friday morning he left without inviting me to wherever he was going. He returned right before the sunset to get his things. After he gathered all of his belongings he gave me a handshake and a hug before he left. He barely hugged his own girlfriend, so I was caught off guard when he reached out to hug me. The weird feeling I had about Leroy escalated when I went the entire weekend without hearing from him. I checked his normal hangout spots and by his place, but he was nowhere to be found. Everything came to a head late Sunday evening.

My mom usually stood while she talked on the phone and was very expressive with her hands. When the house phone rang, she rushed to pick it up because it was the normal time she talked on the phone with her friends. After she answered the phone she took a seat across from me at the kitchen table. A few seconds later she dropped her forehead in her hands, then passed me the phone as if she didn't want it anymore. Leroy was on the other end of the phone calling from the county jail. Leroy and I had such an established rapport that we spoke in code fluently. He was locked up for a murder charge that he said he had no parts of. It was amazing that he was able to communicate that and also tell me that he had a stash of drugs hidden without speaking too recklessly on the phone. Even though Leroy expressed his innocence, he made it seem as if he wasn't getting released from jail anytime soon. Leroy told me to check on his drugs periodically and that I could sell some of it in case I needed money, but he knew there was no chance I would do that. I guess I knew what handle business meant now. I was shook after we got off the phone because I did not know what to believe. Also I did not know who he was charged of killing and if the people would come after me for retaliation.

When I returned back to school my history teacher recommended that I should be reassigned to special education classes and that I get on medication to control my behavior. My mom showed little resistance throughout the process. I was scheduled to take an evaluation on my father's birthday. The combination of anger from my intelligence being insulted and pain from not being able to celebrate my dad's birthday with him caused me to bomb the test. I didn't think much of the evaluation because I always maintained good grades and what I was going through in my personal life. The school thought everything of the evaluation and placed me in special education classes. Once word got out that I was in special ed, people would stop by my classroom door and make fun of me. I had to sit in one class the entire day besides lunch time. We didn't even switch classes when the bell rung. I was alienated and began to question myself if I really had problems or not. Trent began avoiding me once I began taking special ed classes, so I began to socialize with the people in my class. There were sixteen of us. Three had down syndrome and two were crack babies. The other ten and myself had a few things in common other than our skin color. All of us had problems at home, no father figure in the household, and outgoing personalities. By the spring semester I became emotionally drained from being in special education. My teachers made it apparent that they didn't think I had the ability to be successful academically and the teasing from the other students became overwhelming. At the end of the year I decided to drop out. I worked several minimum waged jobs for the first few years after I quit school, then found a steady position at a fast-food restaurant for several years near the Williamsburg. Leroy was in jail during all of those years and had just came home the day before he showed up on Nicki's porch waiting for me. I didn't touch his stash the entire time and checked on it periodically. Knowing that I could marry the woman of my dreams if I made more than minimum wage tempted me to start selling drugs. Leroy coming home seemed like the perfect timing.

Part 3

As we walked to the corner store Leroy and I kept reexamining each other. His appearance had changed. Even the look in his eyes changed. I could tell he had been through some things since we last seen each other. He gained thirty pounds of muscle, cut his dreadlocks off, and had a bald head. He was also a few skin tones lighter than when he first went in. I wore a low haircut my entire life until Leroy went to jail. After Leroy went to jail, I grew dreadlocks to pay tribute to him. We did not get past small talk while we were on the way to the corner store. I had a million questions I wanted to ask, but I decided to approach the situation with caution. Once we exited the corner store and made our way towards Leroy's stash I said, "Man that's crazy how you and Tony switched places like that. How did that shit happen?" Leroy lit a cigarette, then began talking. For the first few seconds I could not comprehend anything he said because of how he was talking with a cigarette hanging out of his mouth. I was more blown away that he was talking with a cigarette on his lip, than him actually smoking cigarettes. He never smoked cigarettes before he went in. When I realized I didn't comprehend anything I asked Leroy could he repeat himself. Leroy cut his eyes at me then said, "It's a long story. I might as well run it from the beginning."

"While I was sitting outside at the church of my uncle's funeral, Tony came outside to check on me during my lowest moment. Ain't no one showed my uncle true love while he was still alive besides you, me, and Tony. People were all in the church acting like they cared about him. Some people pretended like they cared while he was alive, but it was just for ulterior motives. He told me that if he died before me, don't have his services at a church and don't play that racist ass song, Amazing Grace. It pissed me off so much because our family wasn't even close enough to him to know that. For a week straight after the funeral Tony began to look out for me the same ways my uncle would. He would take me out to eat, share knowledge, and give me money. That went on throughout the whole summer. The day you moved back home, Tony took me out to eat. Once we pulled back up at my place to drop me off, he hit the lock button when I tried to get out of the car. It was a loud silence after he locked the doors. Once the doors were locked he lit up a blunt. It was the creepiest smoke session I was ever a part of. He looked forward the entire time until the blunt went out. After he threw the roach out of the window he said, "I know who killed your uncle." My ears began to ring after he told me he knew who was responsible for my uncle's death. I was looking at him while he said it, then turned forward after he delivered the news that I desperately wanted to know. I wasn't sure that I would ever find out who did it until Tony said something. We sat there facing forward and didn't even hear the second line band that passed right by our car. After ten minutes of my insides burning up, we turned our heads to look at each other and both of our faces were filled with tears. In a cold voice he said, "Don't worry, we will handle business." When I exited his vehicle I was unsure of what handle business meant, but the loss of my uncle made me down for whatever. After time went by, I realized that I wasn't down for whatever. The reason I spent the week by you when you were suspended from school was to hide from Tony. While I was taking out the garbage at your place that Thursday night, Tony walked up on me out of nowhere and told me he would pick me up at my place the following night at that same time. Friday night Tony didn't call, but I knew he would be outside of my place when he said he would. When I stepped foot off of the porch, Tony got out of his car. The entire car lifted when he exited the vehicle. He was dressed in a stonewash blue jean jacket, black jeans, a black beanie, and little gold chains around his neck. He left the driver's door open, then walked around the back of the car and sat in the passenger's seat. It went without saying that he wanted me to drive. I never even seen him in a passenger's seat prior to that night. Once I started driving, he directed me towards the Williamsburg projects. The only time he spoke during the entire ride was when he gave me directions on where to turn. When we arrived to our destination, the neighborhood looked very familiar. It was only a few blocks away from where Uncle Gee got murdered. He guided me to a side street that had broken street lights on the corner. We parked at the end of a two way street a few feet away from the stop sign. Right after I put the car in park, Tony checked behind us as if he were checking to see if the coast was clear. He exited the vehicle and whispered, "Open the trunk and wait right here." Then this box head motherfucka squatted low and duck walked across the street like he was a navy seal or some shit. The street was so dark that I couldn't see him again until he opened the side door of the house directly across the street from us. Six gunshots went off back to back with no delay in-between them. Everything went blank until the passenger's door opened and a man with a ski mask yelled, "Pull off! Pull off! Turn left!" A left turn would have sent me up a one way street, but that was a safer option than ignoring the instructions of a man with a hot gun in his hand. I was so shook that I couldn't even tell if it was Tony behind the mask. Even if it was Tony, I did not trust him with my life because he took me on a hit without telling me and the streets are a dirty game. I then seen family members turn on each other before, so I couldn't put it past him that he wouldn't turn on me and do me dirty. He guided me onto the interstate, then took his mask off once we merged on. Tony stared at me for an uncomfortable amount of time, then guided me to a lavish gated community on the east side of the city. Once we made it to our destination, we pulled into the garage of a house that had to be worth seven figures. Tony stared into my eyes as if he were looking for something, then told me to follow him. He led me to a room on the second floor and said, "You and my son are the same size. I have some outfits for him that he hasn't worn yet in his closet. Shower up and change, then meet me downstairs in thirty minutes." I couldn't let the uncomfortableness set in. It took me ten minutes to shower and change. I sat in the bathroom dressed, gone out of my mind wondering what would be the outcome of that shit. On the 29th minute I walked downstairs. While I was walking down the stairs I noticed that his place had cameras almost everywhere. Tony was sitting at the kitchen island in a different outfit. He asked me did I want food, but my appetite wouldn't even let me chew a piece of gum. I turned down the food then he said, "Ok let me take you back home." Not a word was said during the entire ride to my place. When we pulled up to my crib he looked at me then said, "It will be in our best benefit for you to keep silent about this." That killing made the news the next morning. Later that day they arrested me while I was parlaying through the hood minding my business. They didn't arrest Tony until a month later. He only stayed in jail for two months before he was able to bail out. They never even gave me a bond. Although he dragged me into that situation, I stayed solid and didn't snitch on him. My bread was low, so the only lawyer that I could afford was a public defender. The lawyer kept trying to force me to take a lengthy plea deal, but I wasn't about to cop a plea for something I didn't do. They kept pushing my court dates back and lowering the plea deals, so I felt I had a chance to beat it. When it was time for trial they had something on me that I didn't know about. A picture of me and my girl had fell out of my pocket when I got changed at Tony's house that night. The prosecutors didn't have much until then. The last deal they offered me was twenty five years. I really considered accepting the plea. The unexpected happened a few days later. Tony's privileged ass had high powered attorneys, so he actually had a chance to beat his case. I don't know if it was God, my uncle's spirit, or what type of coming to Jesus moment Tony had, but he fessed up to the whole thing. He even confessed that he kidnapped me and committed murder. They only gave him fifteen years, but that spared me. The judge told me I should be thankful for his plea. It was crazy that they told me I should be thankful for a man that cost me several years of my life. My life could never be the same anymore. My face and charges were all over the internet and newspapers. Everyone sees me as a savage now. The only thing that turned me into a savage was jail, but that was the only way to survive in there. Ain't nobody trying to hire me now. I am glad you didn't touch what I left stashed away or I would be fucked up right now. My child support still accumulated the whole time I was in jail. I gotta pay that shit off or I am going to be right back in jail."

When we made it to the abandoned house where Leroy's stash was he said, "Man, I can't believe you ain't set up shop while I was locked down. Why do you want to hop in the game now?" I looked at the sky in disbelief then said, "It's last resort. Even if I worked two jobs it still won't be enough to make ends meet." I followed Leroy as he walked through the front gate and he told me to wait outside, as if I didn't know where the stash was. I guess jail had lowered his trust for people. While Leroy went to get his stash, I wondered why he would take a penitentiary chance right after he just got out. We both had the same reason, desperation to survive.

Once Leroy made it to the side yard, he slid under the abandoned house like he was an experienced plumber. After he retrieved the dusty duffle bag, we made our way to his ex-girlfriend's place. Leroy had a menu of drugs to choose from. "What do you want to move first?" he asked. He had crack, weed, pills, and heroin. After I didn't respond he said,

"I am going to start you off with an ounce of trees. I know you don't know what you are doing, so I am going to school you right quick. A lot of people are going to hit you up for grams. If they ask for a gram give them 1.2 because ain't nobody else in the hood showing love like that. If you show them extra love like that they are going to keep coming back to you for the same bag. The more grams you sell at once, the less profit you make. Don't show extra love on anything 3.5 grams and up. People are going to think shit is sweet and might try to jack you. *Leroy phone rings* Give me one second let me catch this." The drug talk was over my head and I was beginning to change my mind on partaking. The size of his ex's place was slightly bigger than a studio apartment sectioned off into rooms, so I was able to tell that it was a collect call from the penitentiary. The voice on the other end sounded like Tony's, but I was not sure. Once Leroy reentered the room he desperately said, "If you let me borrow your car tonight, I will let you hold two ounces and you could keep the re-up money." All Leroy had to do was ask to use my car and I would have said yes without asking for anything in return. When I tossed him the keys he acted as if I tossed him a bag of gold. Before we parted ways he said, "Good looking out little brother, I will bring it back to you tomorrow night."

On the way to Nicki's place, I realized that I didn't have anywhere to bag up the weed. My intent was to have Leroy do that. The weed was too loud to bag up at my mom's or my girlfriend's crib, plus I didn't want anyone to know that I was selling drugs. An opportunity presented itself to make some money when I turned onto my court. Three dudes around my age were sharing a blunt slightly bigger than a roach. I looked at them as if I had something to say, but nothing came out. One of the three asked, "What's up? You have one?" I didn't know if he meant one blunt, one gram, or one ounce. I shook my head and said, "No, I wish." The same guy quickly responded, "Oh alright." That was his way of subliminally asking me to keep it moving. I had to be the worst drug dealer in the world.

I carried on inside and my little ones were sitting at the dinner table waiting on their food. At night was the only time I felt comfortable being at my family's place. Our old social worker told us that her job wasn't to investigate, but our new social worker acted like she was a secret agent. Nothing compared to being under the same household with my children. That night upped my sense of urgency to move back home.

When the alarm clock rang at six in the morning I hit the snooze button because Leroy still had my car and I wanted to help my kids get ready for school. About an hour after my little ones went to school, Nicki and I heard quick repetitive knocks at the door. My paranoia ballooned because I had drugs on me for the first time in my life and the knocks were unexpected. I assumed it was the police or either the three guys I bumped into the day before. The family police were behind the peephole. My girl signaled me into the closet. I rushed to grab my bag and didn't even get a chance to get fully dressed before I hid in the closet. The heater was broken during one of the harshest winters ever. It was the worst time to be laying in a closet with only a du-rag, tank top, and one tube sock on. Although I was in earshot of the conversation, I was too nervous to listen at what was being said. As the footprints neared, I had no choice but to listen. "Have you moved on from your children's father? I see you have some male boots laying around in this apartment." said the social worker. Nicki responded, "No that's my cousin's boots." In a skeptical manner the social worker said, "Ms. Jenkins, don't let me find out your children's father has been living here. The state sure wouldn't like to hear that." I felt defenseless listening to the whoopee cushion head ass social worker bully my girlfriend.

Leroy went that entire day without returning my calls. I went by his place after I got home from work, but he was still nowhere to be found. It was no big deal because I trusted him and I had more important things on my mind. As I walked away from Leroy's place, I began to feel guilty about what happened earlier that morning. I also felt the social worker might try to win employee of the month by spying on my whereabouts, so I decided to spend the night by my mom. When I plopped on her couch she looked at me with concern then asked, "What's wrong?" I responded by turning over and going to sleep.

The following morning I woke up a few hours before my alarm clock to use the bathroom. When I laid back down on the couch, I heard several hard coughs on the other side of the door. Leroy was on my mom's porch smoking a cigarette like it was the last one left on earth. I was still tired and wasn't expecting his company, so I laid back down. After thirty minutes of in and out sleep, I got back up to check if he was still there. As soon as I peeked out of the curtains, Leroy flicked the butt of his cigarette then began to pace around as if he were in an imaginary box. The sun had not risen yet, that was the only time it was silent in the neighborhood. Any other time you could hear chatter, gunshots, laughs, or arguments. Sometimes you could hear several of those things at once. The silence in the air gave me a chance to hear Leroy mumble curses under his breath, as thick smoke blew out of his mouth. I could not disrupt this unnatural occurrence. I watched him for a few minutes, then got ready for work. When I opened the screen door Leroy hopped off the porch onto his feet then said, "What's up blood? I came to bring you back your keys." I wanted to ask why he was late, but I could tell that he was going through it so I didn't question him. I invited Leroy inside because I had an hour to spare, but he declined as if he had somewhere else to go. After he tossed me my keys, he walked off at a pace much faster than usual. As Leroy disappeared into the cold winter morning, I came to the realization that the old him may never reappear.

To kill time I turned on the news. The 300th murder of the year occurred near the Williamsburg. Nicki wanted me to drop off a bag of baby clothes to her cousin that lived near the murder scene. I was reluctant to go, but good thing her cousin's house was around the corner from my job. I had a few surprises waiting for me when I opened my car door.

Ashes were in the cup holder, crumbs of food were spread throughout the car, and mud prints were on the floor of every possible seat in the car. I was uncomfortable for the first ten minutes of my drive and couldn't figure out why until I slammed on my brakes because the car in front of me braked at a yellow light. I was almost unsuccessful at slamming on my brakes because the driver's seat was scooted further back than usual. Leroy was three inches taller than me, so we could not drive with the seat in the same position. Another surprise was waiting for me under the seat when I reached down to pull the driver's seat forward. The handle of a 9mm pistol was poking out from under my seat. The sight of the pistol caused me to freeze, and people behind me began to blow their horns. A man pulled on the side of my car and yelled, "The light ain't going to get any greener jackass!" then flicked me the middle finger. A police car in my rearview mirror made me snapback to reality. I didn't have time to turn back around to dispose of the gun, so I decided to continue on to drop the clothes off. Initially I was worried about the police car following me, but he turned onto the street after the signal light. A dark grey sedan seemed to do what I thought the police car would do. The grey car trailed every move I made until I did a maneuver to lose them that I learned from watching a high speed chase on the news. The people in that car could have been honestly minding their own business, but my state of paranoia convinced me that they were following me.

I called Nicki's cousin to come outside when I was a few blocks away so I could give her the clothes and hurry to work. Of course she wasn't ready when I pulled up to her house. Two minutes went by and it felt like twenty, because I was cutting it close to make it to work on time. As she hurried to my vehicle, a car resemblant of the one that I thought was following me passed on the street at the end of the block. I was parked at the beginning of the block, so I couldn't tell if it was the same car. My girl's cousin ran her mouth about gossip while I was giving her the bags of clothes. I listened to her for about ten seconds after I gave her all of the clothes, then cut her off and told her I had to rush to work. As she reentered her house I changed shifts then heard a loud streaking noise. After I couldn't detect where the noise was coming from I put the car in drive. When I pulled off the streaking noise got louder and a guy with a black hoodie and a white hockey mask on hanging out the passenger's window of a grey car began firing shots in my direction. I backed over the stop sign and the grey car tried to pull over in the middle of the block. Before the car could park, I pulled the gun from under my seat and began to fire back at the vehicle. After a bullet broke their back window, the car sped off. It was a great thing that they sped off when they did, because the clip was emptied after four shots. I was thankful that my car was still running so I could leave the scene as soon as possible. Once I peeled off and ran back over the stop sign, sirens sucked the air out of my body and chilled my heart. A police car was nowhere in sight, so I floored the gas pedal but my car stopped halfway up the street because of flat tires.

Although I fired several shots in broad daylight, I did not believe that my next move would be jail. The cops swarmed around my car as if they were flies on an overflown dumpster. I felt arrested before they got out of their vehicles. As soon as my left foot hit the ground I was slammed against the back door. My wind was knocked out immediately. Before I could catch my breath, an officer with a strong southern drawl yelled, "Get on your fucking knees!" I was already to my knees and couldn't go anywhere else. After he arrested me, I was pushed to a police car that was parked two cars behind mine. As I was shoved to the police car, chatter began to escalate throughout the neighborhood and more people began to walk towards the scene. When I made it to the back of the police car, the officer pushed me into the backseat then tried to slam the door. My feet were not all the way in, so they got slammed by the door. Once it popped back open, I moved my feet out of the way and the officer slammed the door closed even harder. Shortly after the officer sounded his siren, he pulled off.

I sat in complete silence for the first five minutes of the ride. It really started to hit me that I was going to jail once we got on the interstate. I began to talk to the officer when we merged on, but he acted as if I were invisible the entire ride. After we exited the vehicle at central lockup, he finally said something. He looked at me in disgust then said, "I ain't your lawyer and get it in your mind that none of these other inmates and officers ain't your lawyer either. I hear these sob stories almost every single day talking about, oh, I ain't do it and it wasn't me, and we got the wrong guy. To be honest, you could be telling the truth, but I don't give much of a fuck. Not even a half of one." Everything went blank from the end of his speech, until it was time to take my mugshot and give my fingerprints.

Part 4

Being in jail for the first time was like being reborn again. It was an entirely new world. I subliminally surveyed the room by stretching in different directions to see if I knew anybody in the holding area. The room was filled with people who I had never seen before. My first cognitive thought was to call Nicki. Other inmates were hovering around the phone, so I decided to wait until the area cleared up. For thirty minutes the area around the phone didn't lighten. When I finally got a chance to use the phone, none of my calls were answered. Nicki nor my mom picked up. Several hours later an officer ordered us to line up then moved us into another holding area. As we were being ordered to change out of our street clothes into orange jumpsuits, other freed inmates were changing out of orange jumpsuits into their street clothes in a room across from us. It was a full-fledged business and reminiscent to a hotel in the aspect of people checking in and out.

My cell was nothing like a hotel. It was dehumanizing. Twelve people were caged in one cell with two toilets. As soon as I entered, I spotted a bottom bunk in the corner and went straight to it. On my third day in jail I was escorted to court for my bond hearing. Several inmates got their charges read aloud to them by the judge before it was my turn. After an employee from the public defender's office took down some intake information from me, the judge began to list my charges. My mind went blank when the employee asked me who my lawyer was as if he was asking who my dentist or doctor was. All of my charges that the judge read were expected except for the last one. Possession of crack cocaine with intent to distribute. I yelled to plead my innocence, but the judge cut me off by slamming his gavel. That caused an everlasting echo in my ears. The judge barked, "Take that up with your lawyer! Bond set at $150,000." The price of my freedom was unaffordable.

No one answered my calls until my fourth morning in jail. Once my mom finally answered, she yelled that she had seen me on the news and that everyone was talking about me. She was redundant and unstable with emotions for the first minute on the phone. I cut her off and said, "I didn't do those things. All I did was defend my life. I need $15,000 to bail out and a lawyer." My mom responded, "Boy, I ain't got $15. How am I going to get a lawyer with that? We are going to have to let God get you out of this one baby." The rest of our call was an awkward silence. Before the phone hung up my mom said, "I am going to pray for you." It's no telling what I would have told Leroy if we got on the phone. A phone call to him would have been incriminating, so I decided not to call him. My girl had the same narrative as my mom. All she could offer was prayers also.

I spent the first week staying to myself to reduce my chances of getting into anything. I was a whispered about inmate because I had a popular case and I was a new face. I knew time would come soon for people to try to figure out who I was and what I was made out of. After a month went by, I was moved to where I would be staying until after my trial.

There were three floors in the county jail. The higher the floor, the more severe inmate's charges were. Inmates on the second floor were usually facing twenty years at the most and typically nonviolent offenders. Third floor inmates were mostly murderers, rapists, and people that were facing lengthy sentences. Paranoia about me doing serious time set in when they moved me to the third floor. Adapting to my new environment was a must to survive the situation.

My new home was a large open room with bunks almost filled to capacity. When I entered the cold spaced out room, I spotted an open bunk towards the back wall. I kept my eyes on the back wall to avoid making awkward eye contact with anyone while I walked to my new bed. When I put my bag on my bed, a familiar voice that I hadn't heard in a while called me by my childhood nickname. People from my childhood called me Moonlight, because of my dark skin and white teeth. Peanut, a childhood friend, was standing in front of the bunk across from mine. After we made eye contact, he threw his hands up in a warm welcoming manner. I had never been so happy to see someone in my entire life. Peanut was dealt a tough hand in life. Both of his parents died before he was five years old. After they passed away he moved in with his elderly grandmother. On his ninth birthday his grandmother had a severe stroke and he had been taking care of her ever since. When I was in the second grade, I saved Peanut from getting hit by a car. Although Peanut was in the fifth grade at the time and one of the most popular kids in the city, we hung together often after I saved his life. Previous to the almost accident, we never hung together although we were always in the same vicinity. We also played recreation sports for the same basketball program and lived in the same projects. During Peanut's seventh grade year the school that our program used for practice started charging our coaches to use the gym. One night when Peanut's coach couldn't afford for their team to practice, Peanut and a few of his teammates got jumped by people twice their age from the Williamsburg. The next time when his coach couldn't afford for their team to practice, Peanut and his teammates got revenge on the people that jumped them. They also got in trouble because a policeman patrolling the neighborhood watched the entire attack. A month after Peanut and his teammates got revenge, finances caused their coach to discontinue their season. The streets consumed Peanut once the basketball program dissolved. He progressively got into trouble throughout his middle school years, then dropped out in the ninth grade. After becoming a dropout, Peanut accumulated several murder charges and was in and out of jail. Once we finished embracing each other Peanut raised his eyebrows then looked at me from head to toe and asked, "What the fuck are you in here for? You ain't supposed to be in here with me." No one was in earshot of us and it was my first opportunity to vent since being incarcerated, so I told Peanut everything that went down. Shortly after I began talking, he lit up a cigarette and smoked until the end of my story. Peanut stared at the wall for several seconds after I finished talking. Then looked at me and said, "Man I know your case could be beat. You need to hit Leroy up and see what he could do for you since he is the reason you are in here. You are going to be in here for decades with a public defender. Neither one of us should be in here right now. You know I did my dirt in these streets, but they got me in here for some shit I ain't do. I know I am going to beat this. When I get back on the streets and get some extra bread, I am going to put my lawyer on your case."

Peanut had one of the best lawyers in the nation, but I could not wait on his potential freedom to move my case forward. I decided to follow his advice and reach out to Leroy. Word on the street was that Leroy had came up on a good amount of money since I had been locked down. Once Leroy accepted the call, he cut me off every time I spoke and said the same thing repetitively, "Stay solid. Don't say nothing. I got you." After the fourth time he cut me off I yelled, "Do you know how much my bond is? Do you know what charges they hit me with? Do you know how much time they are talking about giving me?" Leroy acted surprised as if he thought I was in jail for jaywalking. After I finished yelling at him, he told me he would handle everything real soon then rushed off the phone.

Three months had gone by and I still hadn't heard back from Leroy. My situation was still stuck in neutral. My court dates were continuously pushed back because the prosecutors weren't ready for trial and there was a new discovery in my case. Each time my court date was pushed back, my heart tore simultaneously. My lawyer didn't sound like he had much of a defense for my freedom anyway. I started to see jail as an ongoing reality. I joined Peanut's clique the same

46

day we reconnected. The group included three other people besides Peanut and myself. Because my commissary was neglected, I had to find other ways to eat. Most of my food came from people who were being extorted by my circle. As a result of the extra food and working out, I gained over twenty pounds since my arrest date. I knew my family would barely recognize me if they ever showed up to a court date.

Two months later I received some great news. My public defender was no longer representing me. I finally had a private attorney. My new lawyer Jason immediately made me comfortable and optimistic. His energy was high and approach was opposite of my previous attorney. He listened to me and reiterated that he would fight until justice was served. After Jason finished introducing himself, I asked him who paid for his services. He was reluctant to tell me, but I told him I had to know before we moved forward. Once he told me a childhood friend paid for his services, we moved forward. When our time was up, we shook hands and he gave me a follow up date with assurance that he would make traction on my freedom. He said his co-attorney would be accompanying him the next time he comes to visit me. Getting a new attorney was the first time behind bars that I felt optimistic and saw the light at the end of the tunnel. Things were going as good as they could go.

When it was time to go to sleep later that night, Peanut whispered something to me, but I couldn't hear him. I asked him to repeat it again and why was he whispering. Peanut came sat on my bed then said, "I can't say what I have to say too loud. You got to keep it on the tuck when you find out your release date. I am getting out tomorrow. The only witness disappeared and the case fell apart after that. My boys in here with me are getting out also." I was speechless once Peanut stopped talking. I didn't feel an ounce of happiness that he was getting out. Not being happy that my friend was getting out of jail was confirmation that I became institutionalized. All I could do was think about what jail would be like without him. Once I realized I was hating, I gave him a hug and congratulated him. I quickly understood why he advised me that it wasn't a good idea to announce your release date.

A surprise was sitting next to Jason when it was time to meet with him. Out of all the licensed attorneys in the state, Trent that I grew up with was his co-attorney. I never felt any type of way about Trent avoiding me after I was placed in special ed, because everyone else in normal classes did the same thing. But then again, I didn't stand up for everyone else like I did for Trent. I would not have been in that situation if I let him fend for himself. I never expected anything in return, except for him to have my back in case I needed him to. What better timing would it be for him to return the favor.

Once I took a seat across from Jason and Trent I refrained from making it obvious that we knew each other. I couldn't sacrifice anything that was working in my favor. Trent proceeded to do the same. He introduced himself to me as if we never met before. Ten minutes into our meeting, Jason stepped out to handle a phone call. While Jason was away,

Trent went the entire time without acknowledging me. After Jason reentered the room he took a seat, then leaned towards me and said, "There is a new discovery in the case. Do you have any idea what it might be?" The sincerity of my shrug spoke to my ignorance of the new finding. Jason sat up and said, "I don't know what the finding is, but it seems pretty serious. They extended an offer of forty years, but we aren't going for that." Trent spoke for the first time since he introduced himself and said, "I think you should just take the forty years. The District Attorney is up for reelection and he doesn't want to appear soft on crime. Plus you will still be in your sixties once you get out. It's really not much to think about." Jason sharply said, "Pump your breaks. We don't wave white flags until the battle's been fought to its last breath." Then he stood up and said, "Let us get to work. We will follow up soon."

Turns out a day before I got shot at, Leroy did a drive by shooting in my car a block away from where I was arrested. I was shot at in retaliation for what he did. My blood was hot enough to boil some eggs in after I received that news. Although the finding decreased the odds of beating my case, there was no chance in hell that I would take a plea for something I did not do. Each plea deal offered during the following two months leading up until my trial date decreased. I was presented my last three options the day before my trial.

Option 1: Lose in court and fall victim to mandatory minimum sentences or a longer sentence. Option 2: Take a plea for four years with credit for time served and become a convicted felon. Option 3: Beat the slim odds and walk free if I was found innocent. When I asked my lawyers for some time to think about it, Trent asked Jason could he speak to me alone. Jason took a deep breath then left the room. After the door shut, Trent said, "Come on man. You had to know this was a destination for you. I'm not even surprised to see you in here. What they are giving you is a second chance that you can't even be so sure that you deserve." The term sellout took on a new meaning. Trent's betrayal of his job duties and actions of those who structured the judicial system to be unjust for people of our own race caused my body to go into a state of vegetation. I went into another dimension until Jason reentered the room.

Jason had a presence and voice that captured everyone's in the room undivided attention. I gained consciousness when he asked, "What are we going to do?" I responded before he could close his mouth and said, "I'll take the four." Peanut was the only person who appeared for my sentencing. Although I had a release date, it felt like I lost the ones closest to me for life. My relationship could never be the same with any of my loved ones. I would have to reintroduce myself to my children. My girlfriend, well ex-girlfriend only visited me twice in county jail and stopped accepting my calls. My mom visited me half that many times and Leroy was dead to me. There was nothing he could do to repair our relationship. Worrying about how life would be after I was free quickly took a backseat when I returned to my bed after sentencing. I knew my time in prison would be different from jail.

It was great running with Peanut when he was in jail, but hanging with him could have easily gotten me into more trouble. After he was freed, I became a prime target for retaliation because of the things he did. Along with the beatings, extortions, and manipulations that he was behind in jail, several people that he killed had family members or friends behind bars. Regardless of my actions, or lack thereof I was still seen as a part of his crew. It was imperative that I hung with the right people at my next destination.

Breathing in fresh air while walking to the bus that was shipping me five hours north to my new home was like heaven gracing my lungs. In jail we were usually allowed to go outside five times a week. That winter we were only allowed to go outside one day a week. Breathing outside air, which was previously an unconscious everyday routine, was now a luxury. When the bus pulled off, I almost immediately felt sick. Other cars were flying past us, but it felt like I was in a spaceship after we merged onto the interstate. I couldn't believe how long it had been since I was in a moving vehicle. My sickness did not settle until I woke up when it was time to get off the bus at prison.

Part 5

The prison I was shipped to only had a few inmates who were from the same city as me. Because of that, I gravitated towards them. After one week, I finally had a clique to run with. My new clique consisted of five people other than myself. Caron was the youngest in the group. He beat a double murder charge and got sentenced to a six year bid for manslaughter. We arrived to prison together on the same bus. Although he was only seventeen years old at the time, he had been in the system for several years. Purse snatching, assaults, and burglaries kept him in and out of jail before he was a teenager. His conversations usually consisted of him talking about committing the same crimes again on the streets, but executing them better so he won't get caught again. If prisons did yearbooks, he would have been unanimously voted most likely to get arrested the quickest after his release. He was a menace to society and one of the few people that I came across that I actually felt belonged behind bars.

Reggie was the next youngest in the group. He was one of the people that no one expected would wind up in prison. Reggie grew up with both of his parents in the household. Throughout Reggie's entire years of schooling, he only attended private schools and never lived outside of a gated community. His father was a big time gambler that owned several popular car dealerships and his mother was a nurse. Reggie's father had several felonies, so he wasn't able to get life insurance. With no life insurance policy, a cold gambling streak, and debt, Reggie's father didn't leave much behind for his family after he died. Reggie was fifteen when his dad passed away. Even though Reggie's dad had a record, he was the epitome of a perfect father and you would have never assumed he had ever been to jail. He was a legend on the streets and admired by everyone he came across, plus others who had only heard about him. Reggie envied the respect in the streets that his father earned and lusted for it. He had the same entrepreneurial spirit and finesse that his dad possessed; therefore he was successful with flipping the money that his father left behind for him. At sixteen, Reggie aligned himself with some of his father's alliances that were still in the streets, and established himself as a popular drug dealer throughout the city. He had a nice run in the streets for several years. Reggie inherited something else from his father, but it wasn't beneficial. He inherited his father's haters also. One specifically had a larger amount of hatred than others. The one hater that stood out from the rest was an old man that hustled for majority of his life, but had nothing to show for it. Every time he would come up, something would always happen to make him fall off. After Reggie's dad died, the old hater was on the come up again until Reggie stepped on his toes and started hustling in his territory. Once Reggie did that, the old head felt he needed to take action. He snitched on Reggie and got him taken off the streets on his twenty-first birthday. Reggie had a hard time in jail until he realized that he had something that most people don't have in jail, money. His entrepreneurial side kicked in again once he realized that. He put other inmates in position to get money and gained respect from doing so.

Smooth was the next oldest in my new circle. His name said it all. Smooth rarely talked much and had females on a string. It was rumored that he was having sex with several of the female prison guards. He also used other male guards to bring in contraband. The story on how he ended up in jail blew my mind. Smooth and his girlfriend met the first day of his freshman year in high school. Her mother had no problem with their two year age difference. On Smooth's seventeenth birthday, his girlfriend's mom threw him a house party. Several hours before the party she invited him over to help set up. When Smooth got to the house she influenced him to drink some tequila for the first time. Two drinks and thirty minutes later, she invited Smooth to her bedroom to change a lightbulb. Once they got behind the bedroom door, she took advantage of him and they had sex until it was time for her daughter to return home. During the entire party it was apparent that something was wrong with Smooth, but he blamed it on the drinks. Having sex with his girlfriend's mom hurt him more than getting drunk for the first time. When Smooth came over that following Saturday she made several advances at him. After he shut her down on the third try, she told her daughter that she would be sleeping out that night. Two hours later her mother called the police and told the authorities that a grown man was sleeping with her fourteen year old daughter. At that time Smooth was a top basketball recruit and an excellent student. His future was unlimited. His loyalty to the street code was unlimited also. Smooth had a chance at beating his case if he would have snitched on his girlfriend's mom, but he refused to snitch and took a ten year prison sentence on the chin instead. He was scheduled to get out in several months.

The next oldest in the clique was a middle aged drug addict that went by the nickname Rev. He was sentenced to twenty years because of his drug use and fell victim to mandatory sentences. Drug possessions were the only charges on his record. His mother used drugs while she was pregnant with him. Rehab would have probably been a more appropriate place for him. He was punished for how he was brought into this world, not for being a threat to it. No one is granted sympathy behind bars, but Rev had the closest thing to it because he was the minister of the church and his sermons got the hardest inmates attention. Not one preacher from any mega-church in the country could touch Rev in the pulpit.

The oldest member of the group went by the name Lifer. He had several different aliases. At this facility he went by Lifer because he was the only person in our camp that had a life sentence. He was one of the best con-artists that ever graced this earth. Lifer had an extreme sense of passion and conviction when he talked. Even when he didn't know what he was talking about, he made it sound like he was an expert on the topic at hand. Although he was full of shit, he gave some valuable gems on a daily basis. Lifer had been convicted of almost every crime in the book. White collar crimes, violent crimes, arson, possession, manslaughter, and distribution were all on his extensive record. The irrational balance of his criminal history spoke volumes about his unbalanced personality.

Things went smooth for the first several weeks in prison. Throughout the day I spent most of my time with Lifer. He was more preoccupied with learning, rather than working. Working for fractions of the minimum wage was not in my interest either. My mind was on learning so I could finally make above the minimal wage for the first time in my life once I was set free. Reggie and Smooth took daily risks to get time added onto their sentences. Caron was a walking time bomb and Rev was too much of a user for me to hang with. Because of how Caron, Rev, Reggie, and Smooth spent their time behind bars, Lifer became the closest to me out of the group. Staying out of trouble and being able to pick his brain furthered my motivation to hit the ground running after my release. His knowledge seemed like it was the only reformation I would get in prison.

After a few months went by I began to feel like things were too good to be true. I could feel it in the air that changes were on the horizon. Word got out on a Sunday morning that the weights on the yard would be taken away from us. Monday morning the rumor proved itself to be true. The topic of the day in prison made it to the Monday night local news. They interviewed local citizens who all had strong opinions about us having weights. "They shouldn't be able to enjoy themselves because of the crimes they committed." "I don't want my tax payer dollars going to them lifting weights." "It's time to get tougher on criminals." "They will turn into super criminals." "I don't even have a gym membership, why should they get one?" All of the people that they interviewed seemed to have something in common. They were poor, Caucasian, and uneducated. They stood in front of homes that were almost less desirable than where I was jailed. The only thing that made their homes more desirable was the privacy. Each interviewee struggled with subject verb agreements and their words were tough on the ears. Sitting back watching the news that night made me realize that the media will interview whichever people they feel are most adequate to push the agenda they are aiming to get across. Whenever something happens in the hood they find the most intellectually challenged people in the neighborhood to make statements in front of the camera. For this agenda the media gave a platform to the most passionate racists that were ignorant about the topic at hand.

While the intellectually challenged were being interviewed, Smooth was texting a million miles a minute. His mood lowered with each word he typed. After Smooth put his burner phone away he told us that one of the guards he was having sex with gave him a heads up that we would be on lockdown the next day. Smooth was barely strong enough to block the sun out of his face, so I was convinced that something else was the reason for his mood change. He had been acting different for a week leading up to that night, but after he received those texts he was in obvious despair. Everyone else was too concerned with the news to notice. Smooth and I were cellmates, but our conversations never got that deep. He was on the quiet side and mostly communicated with women when he did feel like speaking.

That next day on lockdown I was glad to get a break from Lifer. The silence in the cell with Smooth became uncomfortable after the first few hours. I couldn't let any more time go by without knowing what was wrong with him. Initially I thought I would have to pry to get the real answer out of Smooth, but I was happily mistaken. While I was sitting on the edge of my bed facing Smooth's bed I asked, "Smooth what's going on in your world? You ain't been yourself this past week." Smooth was lying on his back. He put his magazine down, then sat on the edge of his bed and said, "Last week I got a little news that my parole hasn't been accepted yet. They can't tell me why right now, but it's probably because the only address I have to provide them with is my grandfather's house and he lives across the street from an elementary school. I have to register as a sex offender, so it's illegal for me to live close to any schools." I couldn't disguise my anger that he had to be placed on a list with some of the sickest predators on this planet and that his parole might not be granted. Smooth was very unemotional as if he weren't delivering bad news. He looked at me once he stopped talking, but I was staring at the ground speechless and fuming at what he said. Smooth broke the silence then said, "And on top of that, I been feeling sick as fuck this past week. It's probably just stress from not knowing when I'm getting out of here." While still staring at the ground I asked, "How much longer would you have to stay in prison if they don't approve your release?" He laid back down and said, "Two more years man." Not much else was said between us for the rest of that day on lockdown. Smooth opening up to me strengthened our relationship. That night was a tough one to sleep through. Smooth's repetitive coughs kept me tossing and turning until it was time to wake up the next morning.

One day away from Lifer wasn't enough. I wasn't in much of a talking mood after finding out that Smooth might not get out soon. One of the worst things about jail is that there is nowhere to hide. I hung in my cell to avoid Lifer, but he eventually found me. I searched for a way out of the conversation shortly after it began. Once Lifer brought up a friend who did him wrong, I saw my way out of the conversation. Leroy's cousin was an electrician and Lifer had turned me onto some books and knowledge about being an electrician. Leroy owed me more than a favor, so I decided to reach out to him so he could plug me in with his cousin once I got out. Leroy and I spent fourteen of the fifteen minutes I was allowed on the phone talking as if we were best friends and he wasn't the reason I was in prison. When the operator announced that we only had one minute left Leroy said, "Hey do you know umm... What's his name? He is from downtown and brown skinned. Jammed up in there on this dumb ass charge. I think his name is Smooth. Do you know him?" In an excited manner I responded, "Yeah, yeah, I know him! What's up with him?" Leroy said, "Oh I was just asking. Nothing too serious." "Were you locked up with him?" I asked. He responded, "Nah I wasn't. I was just asking if you knew him." "Why though?" I pried. Leroy didn't say anything then the phone disconnected.

As I walked back to my cell, it bothered me that Leroy came off as if he were being messy. Those thoughts consumed me until Lifer unsolicitedly reappeared back in my cell. "What's wrong youngster?" Lifer asked. He opened up to me often about personal things and I hadn't opened up to him about anything yet, so I decided to tell him what was on my mind. "I just finished talking to the guy that's responsible for having me in here." Before I could get my next sentence out, Lifer interjected, "What did he say?" "He bullshited me for fourteen minutes, then asked did I know Smooth and acted like he asked for no reason." I responded. Lifer said, "I know there is a fuckin reason." as if he knew why Leroy asked. Lifer was right though. It was obvious that Leroy was lying and he usually played those type of games. After about thirty seconds of deep thought Lifer said, "He probably asked because Smooth might have your baby mama putting money on his books." Any thought of Nicki put me into my feelings because of how she abandoned me. My thoughts ran rampant about what she was doing while I was locked up. Knowing that Smooth played the lottery and hit the jackpot often, sent me into immediate anger once Lifer put that idea in my head. Playing the lottery meant calling random numbers in the phonebook and trying to establish a relationship over the phone. Hitting the jackpot meant getting something out of the situation. Lifer sympathetically patted me on my back then in a perpetuating voice said, "Don't trip, don't trip. That's the last way you want to react in here. You got to make your move when its least expected. Do everything in your power to not show you know." In my mind it was everything but confirmed that Nicki was sending this noodle built motherfucka some money.

Lifer left out of the cell once Smooth reappeared. Smooth waited for Lifer to leave before he started talking. "Damn I felt like a lab rat in there. They will let me know what's wrong by next week. I am still feeling like shit." I dryly responded, "That's fucked up. I hope you feel better. I think I'm getting sick to." "I hope you ain't feeling like I'm feeling. I wouldn't wish that on anybody." Smooth said, then laid down. I wanted to knock him out before he even laid down, but I wanted the situation to play out so the truth could surface. After I finally fell asleep, Smooth woke me up and angrily asked, "Yoo do you know who touched my magazines?" He asked me as if he insinuated that I touched them. "I have no clue." I responded. He said, "Alright then, bet."

The next day I spent my time being active on the yard and in the library because I had a lot on my mind. The weights would have been perfect to relieve some stress, but they were long gone so curling sandbags and pushups made due. It was strange not seeing Lifer in the library, but it was even stranger to see him in my cell talking to Smooth when I returned in from the yard. Lifer wrapped up his conversation with Smooth as soon as he saw me, then left. Later that night Smooth and I walked to the cafeteria together without saying a word. Reggie and Rev were the only people talking at our table while we ate dinner. Reggie was selling us dreams about what he wanted to do to the guards because the weights were gone. Rev kept blurting out prayers and scriptures to Reggie to calm him down. Caron, Smooth, Lifer, and I were mum on words. Once Reggie stopped talking shit about things that would never happen in real life, the table became silent for a few minutes. Rev looked at each of us, then closed his eyes and lifted his hands up then blurted out, "Good Lord, we sit here today as God fearing men asking you to please deliver us back our weights won't you O Lord and Jesu-" "Yo Rev! How about you shut the fuck up before I bless that ass with a shank." Smooth said as if it were a promise and not a threat. The entire table broke into laughter then Smooth got up and walked away.

The next morning Smooth officially got the news that his release was denied. Looked like a part of him died that day. He spent the entire day by himself. Almost everybody felt bad for him except for a few people in our circle. Reggie and Rev showed some concern, but Lifer and Caron didn't care. They cut their eyes at Reggie and Rev every time they mentioned Smooth's case. The time we spent together during chow time was much shorter than usual. After about fifteen minutes, Reggie and Rev got up and went their separate ways. Then Lifer and Caron got up at the same time and left together.

For the next several days the non-cohesiveness continued. Lifer and Caron were jointed at the hip which was strange. They were cellmates that rarely hung together outside of their cell. Lifer claimed that Caron would get him another life sentence. Caron claimed that Lifer acted like he didn't have a life sentence and he tried to talk him out of too many things. Reggie and Rev continued on being diplomatic with other inmates for their own personal agendas. Smooth was the only person in the circle left to hang around, but I still felt some type of way about him. He remained sick the entire week.

That following Saturday would be the first time I received a visit at my new facility. I initially wasn't excited to see Nicki, but that changed once she agreed to bring my kids. The day before visitation went by perfect. There was no awkwardness within my circle and the day flew by. Once we got back in our cell for the night, Smooth pulled out a phonebook. I laughed then asked him, "What are you doing with the phonebook?" Smooth responded with a laugh then said, "You don't know about this? That's why your commissary be on the thin side. You gotta get your game up. I get one of my girls who works here to bring me a different phonebook every month. I make a new list of women to call every week. Once they answer the phone I check my options. If they don't hang up right away, it's over for them. The next thing you know they are putting money on my books and pulling up here to come visit me. Why do you think I have a visitor every visitation and my books stay laced? I been calling women from our city a lot lately. You know our city is small, so it's easy to play it off and start a conversation. We always know at least one person in common once we start running it." I kept a laugh on my face while he was talking, but immediately wiped it off when he began talking about calling women from our city. That only intensified my hunch that he might have been talking to Nicki.

The four hours in-between the time I woke up and visitation felt like four days. While I was in line to get searched before my visit, I kept my head down the entire time. The visitation area was a fenced in yard that had picnic tables set up in the middle of it. Guards and inmates were on the grill cooking and serving food that was for sale. As soon as I walked into the yard I spotted Nicki. We locked eyes and I power walked towards her. While I was walking in her direction, everything else was a blur to me. Even if she had done something worse to me than what Leroy did, I would have still been happy to see her. I almost forgot what a woman felt and smelled like. I hugged her for as long as I could before one of the guards made us sit across the table from each other. After my high went down from finally hugging a woman, I realized my kids were nowhere in sight. "Where are my children?" I asked her as we sat down. "If you were so worried about your kids while you were in the streets, then you wouldn't even be in here." she responded. I leaned towards her and whispered, "Do you even know why I'm in here?" She folded her arms and said, "Yes everybody knows why you are in here. It was on the news." I leaned back then said, "Wow, you really believe anything on the news." My sentence was almost over so it would have been the worst time to get into an argument with her. The conversation went silent for about thirty seconds. That was perfect timing to gather myself. I looked at her and smiled then said, "I miss you. I can't wait to come back home to you and the kids. Can you get me a plate of chicken and red beans please?" She rolled her eyes then said, "Yea you can move back in until you get back on your feet, but I don't know about you staying after that. Let me go get you some chicken and give you some time to think about what you did to get in here." As if I had only been in jail for a few hours. All of the inmates had to sit on the inside of the picnic tables that were in a rectangular pattern. It was mind blowing to see my girl and the other women on visits next to the female prison guards. On a regular basis I thought the prison guards at my facility were an 8 or 9 out of 10. After seeing my girl and other women who were on visits, the prison guards rating plummeted to a 2 or 3. Smooth walked into the visitation area as soon as Nicki made it to the line for food. The line was facing where the inmates walked in at. When Smooth stepped into the yard they made eye contact. He smiled and waved at her, then she reluctantly waved back. While she was in line getting my food I told myself I wouldn't ask her how she knew him, but as soon as she put my plate on the table I asked, "How do you know Smooth?" She responded, "I just know him from back in the day." I wanted to ask her what fucking day. I knew her almost my whole life and never heard of him. My need to keep our conversation productive and the smell of chicken made me move on from asking her more questions about Smooth. The rest of the visit went perfect. Her guilt about abandoning me kicked in after she listened to my side of the story of what landed me in jail. Nicki said she figured that Leroy had something to do with it, because he began acting really strange after I got locked up then stopped coming around. I spent the rest of our time laying out my plan to get back on my feet after I got released. It was heartbreaking for her to watch them call me by a number and fully search me when it was time to go back into the facility, but I knew my time in jail was almost over.

Caron and Lifer were waiting outside of my cell after my visit was over. They rarely received visits. Everyone gave up on Caron because he would always beat cases that seemed impossible, then still ended up going back to jail. Lifer received no visits because he had done everyone who he knows in the free world wrong. As soon as we entered my cell, Lifer began running his mouth about some mess. I was open to hanging with them, but I wasn't open to letting Lifer's messy stories alter my mood. Having a great conversation with Nicki was the first time I was happy since I reconnected with Peanut. I laid on my back and started thinking about how things would be after I was free while Lifer kept running his mouth. Caron wasn't doing much but laughing. After about twenty minutes, Lifer and Caron made their way to the yard. Three minutes later, Smooth returned. While Smooth looked through his belongings he said, "I hit the jackpot again. I had a new one come in and lace me up with something. I'm about to go scoop some extra snacks." I responded with a slight attitude, "That's good for you son." In prison, each inmate has a magnifying glass on anything that could be a sign of disrespect. "You got something on your mind dog?" Smooth asked, as if I better tell him. "Everything is good." I responded in a non-bothered manner. "Man who the fuck keeps putting a dent in my magazines?" Smooth shouted as he slapped the wall. He looked at me and calmly asked, "You my cellmate right?" "Uh huh." I responded. He said, "Alright bet." Then walked out of the cell. At that moment I felt like I didn't have any other option but to fight him.

I left the cell shortly after Smooth to go workout on the yard. I wanted to get a workout in before I decided on how I would attack Smooth. Ten minutes into my workout Caron and Lifer approached me. As soon as Caron got within earshot he asked, "Why are you working out so hard? Yo baby mama told you how she knows Smooth?" Lifer laughed then said, "Chill man. Don't ruin the rest of his time in here. You could see he is stressed out." I continued to work out without responding. After they realized I wasn't going to entertain them Lifer said, "Watch your back man. You about to get out soon, but you can't let nobody think shit is sweet on your end. Nothing goes down in here without everybody knowing. I heard that Smooth has been plotting on more than your girlfriend."

Over the next few days tension was at an all-time high. Meals were ate over silence. Smooth continued to stay to himself. Reggie and Rev kept busy independently around the jail. Caron and Lifer were moving around like they were best friends. The idle time caused my paranoia to balloon. I purchased a shank from Reggie for a peace of mind. I was desperate for a conversation, so I invited Lifer in my cell. As soon as I took a seat on my bed and Lifer walked into the cell I said, "Man I keep feeling like someone is going to try me before my release date." Lifer cut me off before I could get my next sentence out as usual then asked, "How much longer do you have left? About six months right?" I responded, "Oh no. I am out next week." Lifer stared at me as if I were a ghost. He didn't budge until I asked, "Are you ok?" He responded, "Yea man. It just hit me hard that you are about to be leaving this place and I'm still going to be here." Lifer took a seat on Smooth's bed then said, "Close your eyes and lay down. I am going to pray to God for your protection while you are still here and after your release." Lifer prayed for an extended amount of time. Every time I thought he was finished he would say something else. I was anxious for him to finish as if he were the family member saying the never ending prayer over the food during the holidays. It sounded like that was his first time ever praying. Lifer left out shortly after he was done. His prayers put me straight to sleep. Noise from Smooth looking through his things briefly woke me up. I asked him is everything good and he responded, "Everything is going to be good real soon. Do you want some snacks?" I was low on snacks and money, so his offer couldn't have come at a better time.

The next morning I woke up about thirty minutes earlier than usual. My thoughts superseded the silence. I only had a few days left in prison, but it felt like I had a year left. Everyone in the group made it to breakfast, besides Smooth. Small talk was a struggle at our table. Reggie and Rev left the table first as usual. After they left, Lifer and Caron looked at me then got up without saying anything. I was beyond sore, but working out was the only remedy for my bad nerves.

When I made it by the workout area Reggie had a mean mug on his face and was posted up with five men who looked like they were in prison for killing people with their bare hands. Once he saw me he smiled and pounded his chest. After about twenty minutes of working out and halfway into a set of pull-ups I felt someone approaching me. I stopped to see if my hunch was right. I didn't see anyone headed in my direction, so I did a few extra reps since I took a break during the middle of my set. After I landed back on my feet from doing pull-ups what I was looking for was fifteen feet behind me. Smooth asked, "Where are the snacks I gave you?" I laughed and responded, "What do you mean where are the snacks you gave me?" Smooth smacked his mouth then demanded, "Man up my snacks or I'm going to cut them out you with this shank." As soon as Smooth said his last word from fifteen feet away, a lighting quick punch landed on my left cheek. When I landed on the ground I saw two people in my peripheral attacking me. I dodged the first person and gave the second person several stabs to the mid-section. I watched Caron die with his eyes open, then several other fights broke out on the yard. The only people I could spot in the brawl were Reggie and Smooth. After Reggie dropped Smooth to the ground with a vicious left hook, several other inmates began stomping Smooth. Almost everyone on the yard was cluttered around the fights. Lifer was standing the furthest away from the commotion smiling and smoking a cigarette. After Lifer and I locked eyes, I heard a loud noise, then blacked out.

Barrel In The Streets Conclusion

Six months after Jamal shanked Caron to death, he received a life sentence. Peanut wasn't able to pay a private attorney to defend Jamal again because he was killed in front of his mother's house two months after he was released from jail. Leroy opened a mechanic shop during the same week that Jamal was sentenced to life. Lifer was paroled two years after Jamal's sentencing.

Lifer orchestrated the entire situation that led to Jamal's life sentence, because of his jealousy about Jamal's potential release date. During each visit to Jamal's cell, he stole several of Smooth's magazines and blamed it on Jamal. Smooth was too sick to get revenge, so Lifer told him that all he had to do was distract Jamal, then Caron and another inmate would take care of the rest. Caron was promised $100 for the attack that he didn't live long enough to collect. Reggie knew about the entire attack. He put two and two together after Jamal purchased a shank from him and overhearing Lifer's plan. Smooth previously snaked Reggie out of $25, so he didn't want to risk his chance to get revenge by giving Jamal a heads up that he would get jumped.

Two weeks after Caron died, Smooth passed away from complications of HIV. The guard who gave Smooth HIV had unprotected sex with several other inmates. Rev is currently finishing out his sentence with the same disease that took Smooth's life.

After Jamal was shipped to a new prison to serve his life sentence, he received some news that sent him into a deeper depression. When Nicki came to visit him for the first time at his new prison, she informed him that Smooth was her cousin. Nicki was initially hesitant to tell Jamal because she wanted to keep Smooth's illness a secret. Three years into Jamal's life sentence he was killed in retaliation for Caron's death.

On the surface Lifer and Leroy appear to be the largest reasons for Jamal's demise. Scratching the surface is a galaxy away from the foundation of the truth. The public school system, parental court systems, and socio-economic factors were the root of his problems. Parenting and the people he surrounded himself with were secondary causes of his demise. Parents' solely relying on teachers to educate their child enhances an environment that's created for malperformance. A parent should know their children's academic capabilities and behavioral characteristics better than their teachers. Jamal's mother was not abreast of her son's academic performance or behavioral characteristics; therefore she let the system have their way with her child. The parental court system let Jamal's mother keep his father out of their son's life.

Whose to say that Jamal wasn't a father figure away from avoiding an early death?

Barrel In Corporate America Part 1

"Good luck on your interview Lawrence. I am beyond proud of you for going against the grain and following your own mind. Now it's about to pay off. Goodnight baby, I love you." My mom said before we got off the phone. She was the only person that backed my decision for college. When I graduated from high school, I was accepted into several Ivy League schools and had several opportunities to play college basketball. Because I am six foot seven inches, everyone felt that I was obligated to continue my basketball career. I hated playing basketball until it made me popular in high school. In middle school I did not have much luck with females, but once my basketball skills made me popular, females began to come out of the woodworks. Even then I had no passion for the game. My real passion was engineering. Most children lose their desire to put things together after they get too old for Legos. After Legos I began to put together train sets, household appliances, and anything else that needed assembling. I spent my entire upbringing living for other people. I saw choosing which college I would attend as the perfect opportunity to start living for myself.

Two weeks before my high school graduation I narrowed my choices down to an Ivy League School and a top ranked public university. When graduation arrived, I still hadn't made a decision yet. A week after graduation things changed. During the summer after my high school graduation I was void of any plans. Most of my peers in the neighborhood already began to travel down the wrong path in life. We were headed in two completely different directions. I was still very accessible to them and they were hard to avoid because we all lived in the same public housing projects. At that time in life, the only time I exited the city limits were for basketball purposes. Once Marcus Garvey University extended an offer to attend a two week engineering program on campus, I accepted before I could hang up the phone. Garvey University was five hours away from the state line. I got the call on a Wednesday and the program began that following Monday. Those next several days felt like several months. Once I broke the news to my friends, they showed no excitement. It rubbed off on me also. Initially I was excited about going out of state to compete at the program, but then I started to second guess the opportunity. I felt what a HBCU had to offer could not compare to what an Ivy League school or a top ranked university could.

When my mother and I arrived at Garvey, I was tempted to get back in the car that she borrowed from her best friend and return home. It took a lot for me to want to get back in that car because of how difficult the ride was to get to the university. I almost strained my bicep trying to roll down the jammed passenger's window. It was stuck the entire ride. During the ride I got rained on and I felt scorched when it wasn't raining because the air conditioner was broken. It looked like I walked there when we finally made it to our destination. After we finished the paperwork in the university's front office, I was instructed to check into the dorm rooms that I would be staying in. The dorms looked like the motels where couples would get busted on the television show "Cheaters". My mom forced me to stay when I tried to renege on the two week program. Anything I did in my life my mom made sure that I stayed the course and executed. I am beyond thankful for the way my mother raised me. Her making me stay was another display of the discipline that she instilled in me. Because of so, I always found it a priority to honor my commitment.

On the third day at the program, my discipline paid off. There were twenty-nine other recent high school grads from public high schools in the engineering program also. Only two other attendees besides myself took the program seriously. The other two who took it seriously were arrogant and hard to get along with, so I remained isolated for the first few days. The program was headed by a middle aged black man named Doc. He was the first black male teacher that I ever had. At the end of the third day in class he told me to stay behind while all of the other attendees were vacating the classroom. As the other students were leaving, I did not know what to expect. I wondered if he was going to tell me something about being anti-social or if he could tell that I didn't want to be there. Once the last person exited, Doc walked into the hallway. After he looked in each direction as if he were checking to see if the coast was clear, he reentered. He walked to the front edge of his desk and took a seat on it then said, "In my twenty years of teaching this program, I have never seen someone take it so seriously. We target students from low performing public schools in poverty stricken areas to help students break generational curses. I read your entry essay, watched you in class, and outside of class. I can tell that you are serious about changing you and your family's life. Your mother must be an amazing woman, and I know she is very proud of you. Most attendees see this as a vacation out of the hood and don't realize the opportunity at hand. Make sure what I am about to tell you stays between us. I am not supposed to be telling you this, but I saw the list of the other colleges you are considering. So I know we might not be that high on your radar, but the winner of this program will get a $6,000 scholarship on top of whatever existing scholarships they have. So if your school is already paid for, you will have an extra $6,000 in your bank account every semester, plus whatever other extra grants and financial aid you may have."

From that day until the end of the program, I worked night and day to finish first and win the scholarship. My initial intent was to live it up every night at the program since it was my first time being away from home by myself. It no longer became tough for me to fight the urge of going out at night and hanging out during my leisure time. Needless to say I won the program and secured the bag. Getting an extra $6,000 a semester put me into a tunnel vision of going to Garvey University. My hood was so cutthroat that my mother was the only person I felt comfortable telling about the extra money I would get with the scholarship. That amount of money would have made me a target whenever I would return back home from school. A week after I returned home from the program, the only friend I had on my high school basketball team was killed in broad daylight while he was walking home. Losing him furthered my desire to hang up my sneakers and move away from home ASAP.

I decided to enroll early and take summer classes at Garvey University. However there was only one problem and it wasn't a small one. My scholarship money didn't kick in until the fall semester. I committed to summer sessions without fully figuring out where I would be living. Being anti-social at the program backfired on me. Most of the people at the summer program were from the city that the college was in, but I didn't make time to build relationships with any of them. A woman that I met at the club on the final night of the program was the only person who I could ask for a place to stay. Although it was a shot in the dark that was the only shot I had available to take.

Part 2

I was initially surprised that she agreed to let me stay. I told her that I would only stay for a few weeks until I figured something out, but I knew it would take longer than that for me to figure something else out. I met Cherry on the final night of the program when I went out to celebrate. Although I knew the chances were slim that I would get to interact with her at the club while she was working, my eyes stayed fixated on her the entire night. She was five feet two inches tall, petite as a gymnast, but was thicker than a bowl of cold grits. Her skin was whisky colored and smoother than apple skin. After she finished delivering bottles to her last section for the night, she slipped me her number. We kept in touch every day after we first met and she welcomed me with opened arms when I asked could I stay by her place.

Things went perfect for the first few days of living together. It was a great adjustment going from living with my mother to living with the finest woman I ever met in my life. On our third night of living together I took Cherry out for dinner at a nice steakhouse to show her my appreciation. During the entire dinner she showered me with financial sob stories. After I took care of the tab she started telling me about her water bill. Once I got the receipt back from our waitress I asked Cherry, "How much is your water bill this month?" She responded, "It's $190 could you take care of that for me boo?" I gave her $200 in twenties then we left the restaurant. She hugged my left arm during the entire walk from the dinner table to my car.

Cherry showed me affection almost the entire drive back to her house. She stopped once we pulled into a gas station near her house. After I got back in the car, Cherry put her hand on my thigh, then asked could I help her with the light bill. Once I didn't respond she said, "It's only $250 baby." I told her I spent all of the extra money I had on her water bill and the porterhouse steak she ordered, then she took her hand off my thigh. I felt like a bigger duck than Donald after I laid down that night. While I laid in bed, everything began to register in my head. She lived in a studio apartment. The only way her bills could have been that much was if she had a waterfall and a jumbotron in her place. Her apartment was so small that you could jump from the back door and land outside of her front door. After she fell asleep I repacked my bags and moved out in the wee hours of the morning.

With zero destinations to arrive at, I decided to park in the faculty lot overnight. That was the only covered parking garage on campus. For one month straight I slept in the faculty lot overnight and woke up at five in the morning to move my car before any of the staff returned for work the next morning. Living out of my car wasn't as bad as it seemed then. Since I was a toddler I always rode the public bus everywhere I had to go. The church I attended since my early childhood gave me a car for graduation instead of a scholarship because my tuition was already taken care of. I was so excited to finally have a car that I did not realize I was homeless until a month after I moved away from Cherry's place. To get by, I took showers at the gym and washed my clothes at a local laundromat. My only worry was not being able to keep my belongings safe in a car that didn't have tinted windows. My belongings filled the front seat, back seat, and the trunk.

I had a heavy paranoia about taking my first midterms in college because they were all scheduled on the same day. No matter how much I prepared, I felt it would be the hardest day ever, so I studied night and day for a week straight until it was time to take the exams. I breezed through my midterms and they were much easier than what I anticipated. My performance called for a celebration. I decided to go to a different club from where I met Cherry to celebrate. After two hours of partying with a few classmates, I decided to step outside of the club to make a phone call. Once I made it outside, I spotted a woman at the end of the block who resembled Cherry talking to someone in a grey foreign car. I walked to the edge of the block to see if it was her. My mind drifted into another world until the person on the other side of the phone raised their voice and asked was I still there. "I'm not. Let me call you back." I responded. The lights were broken on the corner I was standing on, so I was able to watch her in the shadows without being seen. The lights weren't much brighter across the street where Cherry was, but I could see that she was talking to a guy old enough to be her grandpa. Once he gave her a stack of money, Cherry checked her surroundings then got in the car and the old man pulled off as soon as she shut the door. Watching her ride off with a man who could offer her something that I couldn't put me into my feelings. I felt the only way to have a woman like her was to have a lot of money. At that point I came to the realization that I caught feelings for a woman that was out of my league. Once I returned into the club I wasn't able to enjoy myself anymore. After an hour of being in my feelings and trying to numb the pain with brown liquor, I decided to make my way back to the car. I walked to my car in a daze. When I reached down to open the driver's door, the handle was missing along with all of my belongings that were left on the seats. The only belongings I had left were the ones that were in the trunk. I decided not to call the police because I had a few drinks in my system and I was too ashamed to admit that I was dumb enough to leave my belongings visible in my car while it was parked downtown late at night. That one night was more draining than the week leading up to midterms.

The following morning I was awaken by repetitive knocks on my driver's window two hours after my normal wake up time. Doc had a puzzled look on his face, as I laid reclined in my driver 's seat with a blanket on top of me. It was impossible to play it off like I wasn't homeless. "How long have you been living like this son?" Doc asked as if he wouldn't accept anything but the truth. I responded, "Since the first day of summer school." I was too embarrassed to tell him the story about Cherry. Doc took his glasses off then said "Why didn't you say anything? I have several rental properties throughout the city and suburbs. I would have squared you up with something for the summer if you would have opened your mouth." Later that night I moved into a loft downtown ten minutes away from campus and my car got repaired two days later. Doc comped my rent until the fall semester and kept my rent at $500 for the following three years. During my first three years in college I moved with the same sense of urgency I did during the two week program before my freshman year.

Although I was at a historically black college I was one of the only black people in the engineering department. Almost everyone else in the department were foreigners. The legacy of foreign students in the department started two decades before I joined. Students would come from third world countries, then go back home and tell younger students about it. These countries became feeders into the program. People who came from these foreign countries were able to create economical differences in their homelands from the strengthened networks they built by funneling students through the engineering program at Garvey.

Not for a minute did I regret attending Garvey University. Teachers were very hands on, students were prideful about attending the university, and the alumni consisted of a countless amount of inspirational people of my ethnicity that I didn't even know existed. The love I had for my college still wasn't enough to convince others that I made the right decision by not continuing my athletic career or attending an Ivy League school. Many times in life the most popular decision isn't the most informed one. Although validation from others was never a necessity, I always had a chip on my shoulder to prove that I made the right decision to attend a HBCU. At the end of my junior year I was presented a chance to prove everyone wrong.

Williams Commerce, one of the most popular oil and gas companies in the world, reached out to me to apply for an internship with them the summer going into my senior year. Getting a position with Williams Commerce would silence my critics who felt I made the wrong decision to attend an HBCU. Although they personally reached out for me to apply, my confidence was low about landing the internship. The recruiter gave me a heads up that there were over 2,000 other applicants. Only five would be selected to come in for a day long interview process. Two candidates would be awarded the internship that paid $35 an hour and one would be offered a full time position after the completion of their undergraduate degree. During the week of finals I got the news that I was one of the five students selected to attend the day long final interview process.

Part 3

My happy to be here mentality was erased once I got the news from the recruiter that I was one of the five selected. If I was thought that highly of to be selected in the top five, then I knew I had a real chance of securing the internship. Having a reason not to go home for the summer also motivated me to secure one of the two intern spots. The company was only a fifteen minute commute from my apartment. The week flew by leading up until the day of the final interview. I left an hour early to head to the interview because of the car issues I was experiencing at the time. When I arrived forty-five minutes before the interview, I sat in the parking lot examining the facility. It was like Fort Knox to get into and had an amazing campus in the heart of the central business district. Watching all of the foreign cars pull into the employee parking lot while I sat in my hooptee ignited my hunger to secure the internship. Thirty minutes later all of the other participants arrived.

I began to get to know the competition as soon as I entered the front lobby. We were given a sticker with a numerical value to identify ourselves once we entered the facility and an agenda for the day. I was contestant #1. Contestant #2 and #3 were from Ivy League schools. Contestant #4 and #5 attended top ranked public universities. Each contestant besides myself was a Caucasian male. I had yet to see another black person in the facility yet. The entire morning consisted of a group project. We would be given three assignments to complete out loud in front of fifteen employees with the company. Being a team player and communicating with others were always strengths of mine, so I went into the interviewing process full of confidence.

A hierarchy was established within the first hour of the group project. Contestant #2 was one of the smartest people I ever came across, but he was by far the most arrogant person I ever met. He was barely tall enough to ride a roller coaster and had a heavy New York accent. He spoke in a very rushed manner and had little patience. Almost everything he said was in a snobbish tone. Contestant #3 was very shy and did little speaking. He was tall, clean shaven, and well dressed. Although he didn't say much, I assumed he was intelligent because he was a finalist for the internship. He looked the part, but didn't act it. Contestant #4 was very sharp. He had a strong southern accent and communicated well with everyone. Contestant #5 seemed remedial to say the least. He must have been made a finalist by mistake. He added no value to any conversation he joined.

After we wrapped up the group project, everyone in the room disbursed towards the executive boardroom for a catered lunch. The boardroom was everything I imagined one would be from watching movies. It was on the top floor of the building with a glass wall overlooking a view of the city. I did not let the moment get the best of me and acted like I was having lunch in a school cafeteria. Leading up to the interview I felt like I did not belong, but after standing out in the group project I felt as if I belonged and was worthy of the internship. I made it to the boardroom before the other interviewees. When I made it to the boardroom I spotted the first black person I came across the entire day. He was tall, sharply dressed, and appeared on the brink of retirement. His name tag read, Chauncey. He was dressed in a tailored three piece suit with top of the line accessories. My face lit up when I spotted him sitting by himself. I figured establishing a relationship with him would enhance my chances of obtaining the internship. As I began walking towards him he got up from his chair, then put his head in his phone and walked to the hallway. When I made it to the seat next to where he was sitting I was able to see him in the hallway. For five minutes he stood there looking through his phone until others began to enter the boardroom. A panel member by the name of Connor came sat next to me while I was waiting for Chauncey. Chauncey never returned to his initial seat and embraced contestant #2 and #5 as soon as they crossed the threshold. He invited them to sit next to him on the other side of the room. Connor and I established a relationship very fast. We didn't appear to have anything in common besides a passion for engineering and sincerity. He embraced me in a way that I expected Chauncey would. While we ate the rest of our lunch he helped prepare me for the rest of the afternoon.

The next two steps went by smoothly. I knew I would never see my score on the assessment I took after lunch, but I am sure I scored a 100. I breezed through the next round of testing also. The last step was a panel interview with five higher ups. The panel consisted of the CEO, CFO, head of

Human Resources, Connor, and Chauncey. The head of HR and the CEO asked majority of the questions during the panel interview. No reactions were given after each of my answers and everyone wore a pokerface. I began to question my performance mid-interview because of so. Towards the end of the interview most of the panel members appeared to lighten up and I began to feel confident that I would be awarded the internship. "For our final question and maybe our most important Lawrence. Why should we hire you instead of one of the other candidates?" asked the CEO. I looked at her in the eyes and responded, "Every contestant has a similar education as myself, but no one's motivation could compare to mine. Knowing that my family is relying on me has given me a work ethic that is unmatched and also-" Chauncey cut me off and asked, "Does your family not rely on your father?" "No." I responded. I took a deep breath because he stopped me from selling myself on why I should be selected for the internship and I began to think of my deceased father. Connor interjected and said, "You are right about that. I can tell that you have a different level of motivation than most people who come in here as candidates for the intern position. Being highly motivated is a very important quality to have if you want to be a part of Williams Commerce. Thank you for your great effort today. This step is done. Wait in the boardroom and we will have a decision here shortly."

As I made my way to the boardroom I was all but sure that I did not get the internship because of the stunt Chauncey pulled. He tried to expose some of my personal business that

I was not comfortable talking about and had no relevance to the situation. Going from feeling that I secured a life changing opportunity to feeling like I lost it because of someone else caused my stomach to turn. I rushed to the restroom stall furthest away from the door with no need to use it. As I rested my head on the door of the stall to regain my composure, I heard Connor and Chauncey walk through the restroom door. Connor's voice was the first one I recognized. He asked Chauncey, "Which two do you like best out of the five?" Chauncey laughed as if it were a no-brainer and said, "Definitely #2 and #5." "Really? #5 is the biggest douchebag I ever came across. If he gets the internship I might have to leave the company. I think #1 and #4 were the best." Connor responded. The room fell silent for a few seconds. I was glad that the last stall was positioned so they could not tell I was occupying it. Chauncey broke the silence and said, "I could tell #1 has problems at home. Do you know where he is from? I don't think he would be a good fit here. You need to rethink about #5 Connor. He comes from great lineage. His father is the mayor of the city. That can open some doors for some people within the company." Connor cut him off then said, "I don't care if his father is the president, he can't be an intern here and #2 is too arrogant. All hell is bound to break loose if he doesn't get his way." Before Chauncey could respond someone entered the restroom. My heart felt like it got flushed down the toilet after their conversation ceased. Once they left the restroom, I knew I had to rush back to the boardroom for the conclusion of the day.

As I sat and waited with the other contestants for the employees who participated in the interview process to enter the boardroom, I began to make other plans for the summer. Watching the other candidates enjoy themselves made me want the announcements to go by as quick as possible. Once the employees filled the front of the room, Chauncey made his way to the podium with two white envelopes in his hand. I listened to about twenty seconds of his speech, then began to stare out of the window. After he paused for a few seconds I redirected my attention back to him. He broke the silence and said, "Before I announce the two winners of the internship, I want to thank everyone for coming out and giving it your all. Making it this far is an accomplishment in itself. You all should be proud of yourselves no matter what the outcome of today is. Each one of you have a bright future. For the three people who didn't get selected for the internship, you all will still get a prize for being a participant today. A $500 check has already been issued out to those three candidates. The secretary at the front lobby will have your checks waiting for you once we conclude. Without further ado, let's announce the winners."

"For a decade running an Ivy League student has been successful at landing an internship with Williams Commerce. Contestant #3, congratulations! Please meet us in the Human Resources manager's office once this ceremony concludes so we can complete your paperwork." Contestant #2 gave #3 a high five then whispered to him, "We made it baby. Ivy league for the sweep." #2 smirked at us while we waited for them to announce the second winner. Chauncey opened the next envelope and said, "Wow, this is a first." Then looked at the other panel members in shock and continued. "This is the first time a student from Garvey University has been awarded an internship here. Congrats contestant #1. I am looking forward to you joining the staff as the other intern we will bring on for the summer. For the other three who weren't selected, please reapply for next summer and thank you for coming out today." Tears landed on my shoes the moment he said my college's name. After Chauncey finished his last sentence he walked down from the podium and the CEO made her way to the podium. As soon the CEO opened her mouth to speak, contestant #2 flipped over the table he was sitting at and yelled, "This is bullshit! There is no way you all did not select me!" Then left the room. His outburst almost made me forget that I had landed the internship. He must have also forgotten that the company was still giving him a $500 check. Contestant #2 acted as if he was entitled to winning the internship and that the school he attended guaranteed him a spot.

I completed my paperwork around 7:00pm that night. The only people left in the building were a few janitors and higher ups. Once the building was almost fully vacated my emotions began to kick back in. For the most part I held my emotions in at the ceremony because I didn't want to act surprised that I won. Excitement kicked into full gear after I finished my paperwork. When I went back to get my bag that I left in the boardroom, Chauncey was there putting some chairs up. His face lit up when he saw me, then he embraced me with a handshake and a hug. My eyes watered

89

as he approached me. A few tears got on his suit after he congratulated me. After he noticed the tears on his suit he said, "It's ok man, you can let it out. I have about a hundred more of these suits. I was rooting for you the entire time and I am looking forward to taking you under my wing."

I called my mother four times before I could exit the premises to inform her of the great news, but she didn't answer. After my mom didn't answer the phone, I realized that she was the only person I told about the interview. It was urgent that I told someone about my great achievement, so I reached out to Doc to see if he was available for dinner. It was a must that I told him face to face. I was relieved when he accepted my invitation. Doc was the father figure that I always dreamed of having. I couldn't imagine where I would have been if it wasn't for his mentorship. While I was waiting for Doc to arrive, I began feeling bad about not telling him that I was interviewing with Williams Commerce. As soon as he greeted me he asked, "What's going on?" Insinuating that he wanted to know the reason why I invited him to dinner such last minute. "I got an internship at Williams Commerce!" I responded. Doc raised his eyebrows then said, "Really? Congrats! That's big time right there. I stopped funneling people their way about ten years ago. They have this man. I can't think of his name. He is a brother to. Chauncey is his name. That jive ass man. Punk ass Chauncey. Ever since he has been head of that program not one black person landed one of those intern positions. A few years ago I heard he got caught with some prostitutes. He is an ideal gatekeeper for that company. They made him step down from being head of the internship, but he was still able to keep his job. I believe a guy named Connor is head of that program now. Do your best to stay far away from Chauncey. He is no good." I didn't want to believe Doc's assessment about Chauncey because I felt I needed his blessing if I were to be successful at the company. But it was easy to believe because of what I heard in the restroom. Doc always looked out for me by telling me what was real, even if it was something I did not want to hear. I had almost forgotten about what Chauncey said when I overheard him in the bathroom until Doc warned me about him. My mood was dampened after he gave me the heads up on Chauncey, so I decided to change the conversation for the remainder of the celebration dinner. Once I made it back to the car, I dialed my mother's number again. This time it went straight to the operator informing me that her phone was cut off. My mom periodically let her phone get cut off although I gave her money for the bill every month. Because I had a four day weekend and I wouldn't be returning home for the summer, I decided to drive back home and visit her the next morning.

Part 4

Normally I blasted music the entire ride when I took a road trip, but that trip I rode in silence. It burned me up that every time I sent my mother money, it would magically disappear shortly after. She was on government assistance and had very few expenses. The blinds were closed in her window, so I wasn't able to tell if she was home when I pulled up to her place. I knocked on her door for about five minutes until the neighbor across the hall opened his door. Her neighbor said, "Hey man she hasn't been home for about a week. You might want to check somewhere on Paris Avenue." I chuckled and said ok. I don't know why he told me to check there. That was a troubled area. An incident on Paris Avenue made the news every week. While I was driving down the avenue looking for any sign of my mother, I spotted the car that my mother drove me to college in. The car that didn't look like it belonged on the road was parked in front of an abandoned house. Gloria, my mother's best friend was a well-known rockhead in the neighborhood. She had a heart of gold, so not many people mentioned her habit. I knew she was probably in the house doing drugs, but it was urgent that I found out where my mother was. I couldn't go another minute without knowing.

I was scared shitless as I approached the crackhouse. The thoughts of what goes on inside of them often entered my nightmares. When I tried to open the front door, it felt like there were about four locks on the door. I ruled out knocking on the door as an option, so my second option was the side yard. I hopped over the gate that came up to my chest because it was locked also. After I passed up the first window on the side of the house, I heard two feet hit the ground then a powerful fist struck me in the middle of my back. The punch dropped me to my knees, then my face was slammed into the fence. A deep voice full of anger whispered, "Ain't nothing back here for you beanstalk. What the fuck you doing here?" As urine trickled down my legs I said, "Man I am just looking for my mom's friend. I think she knows where my mom is." The guy tightened his full nelson grip then said, "Oh, both of those bitches are inside. I am going to tell them you stopped by looking for them." In a petrified voice I said, "Ok, I am leaving." He helped me to my feet and loosened his grip, then I used the back of my size 16 shoe and kicked him between his legs. After he fell to the ground I got on top of him and kept punching him until he was unconscious. I entered the crackhouse through the back door and the first thing I saw was my mother lying next to a spoon and a syringe looking like a zombie. I picked my mom up, then we escaped through the side yard opposite of where the guy I knocked out laid unconscious.

I didn't realize my hand was broken until we were halfway back to my apartment. I might have went the entire ride without knowing if I didn't almost run out of gas. My mom was still high when we made it back to my place. I would have thought she was dead if she did not snore the entire ride. Once we parked in the garage at my place, I dropped my forehead on the steering wheel and cried tears until a puddle formed on the carpet. Everything suddenly began to make sense. As a child things would go missing in our household one by one, and my mom would act like someone broke in and stole it. It made no sense that someone would break in and only take one item. Then she would act as if nothing happened every time something went missing. My mom also had marks on her forearm that she blamed on her being a tomboy when she was a child, but those marks accumulated after I was born. I had millions of questions to ask her, but was too choked up to get a word out. My mother woke up once I laid her in the guest room bed at my place. Once she realized where she was at, she clicked out and began to act irrational. After I bear hugged her in my arms for about thirty seconds, she began crying her heart out on my chest. Her tears dried up about ten minutes later then she asked, "Could I explain everything to you Monday when I gain enough strength to tell you everything." As much as I didn't want to wait that long to hear about what was going on, I accepted it. I made dinner for her then I left for the hospital to get my hand checked out.

My mother was my everything, literally. I never had many friends and the ones that I did have weren't close enough for me to open up with about this. Now I had no one to talk to. I felt in complete isolation. Being isolated is one of the most overrated things in society. People make it seem cool to be alone in the world, but that is a cold and lonely feeling no matter how people try to play it off. Watching a mother play with her son in the waiting area at the hospital caused me to sulk even deeper in my misery. I dropped my head in my good hand, then I felt a familiar touch on my back and a

94

seductive voice ask, "Why are you down handsome?" My heart jumped back to my chest when I saw Cherry's beautiful face. That was the first time we saw each other in three years. It looked like she aged backwards over the past few years. I could see that her butt had gotten bigger while she was still sitting down, and her face looked even more youthful. The compassion and empathy that she showed made her one of the few people I came across in life that I felt comfortable opening up to. She couldn't have reappeared at a better time. We talked as if we hadn't skipped a beat since we first met and held each other's undivided attention until my name was called to be seen. She followed me and continued talking as I walked towards the nurse. Once we got within earshot of the nurse she asked me, "Is your wife coming with you sir?" Cherry answered, "Yes, I am coming with him." I didn't object. From when we first started talking in the waiting area, until the doctor came in to see me, I vented about everything that I was going through to Cherry. When it was time to part ways, I began to regret telling her everything because I had no interest in talking to her again. It was a mental one night stand. Once we made it outside I gave Cherry a hug and thanked her for listening, then told her I would see her around. She invited me to her place, but I declined. It would have taken more than three years for me to forget how she tried to finesse me. Cherry was pressed to get me to come over because she was going to Miami the next day and she claimed that she missed me. After she caught an attitude when I declined her invitation, the feeling of regret solidified itself. Opening up to a person with untrue intentions puts you into a state of vulnerability.

Painkillers and the awkwardness of what happened Friday kept my mom and I in separate rooms for the rest of the weekend. Although we were only fifty feet apart, it felt like we were fifty countries apart. I was speechless with the lady who I was never short on words with. Being that I never let a situation get the best of me, I had to figure out how to get some help for my mother ASAP. There was no time to waste because I was the only person that my mom had to rely on. I couldn't get past brainstorming on what to do because I was too distraught to speak with anyone. I dialed about fifteen different numbers but couldn't hit the call button once. The biggest day of my life snuck up on me real quick. That Sunday night was one of the most stressful nights that I ever experienced. Guilt began to set in that I turned my phone off for the entire week of finals except for when I called my mom to tell her about the interview. It's no telling what one phone call could have prevented. I listened to "T-Ray The Violinist" for the rest of the night and lit a few candles to settle me down as much as possible.

I went to sleep stressed then woke up feeling blessed. I was ready for my first day of the internship. The only thing I wasn't ready for was to explain why I had a cast on my hand. Being one of the only black people in the building and standing six foot seven was already enough attention. The first person I encountered that morning asked me about my hand before they told me good morning. I thought about several explanations, but drew a blank when I was asked what happened to it. After a few seconds of not being able to reply with a reason the person implied, "Oh you were playing basketball weren't you." Normally I despised the attention that my height got, but I was thankful for it at that moment. "Yes exactly, you guessed it." I responded with a fake smile that evolved into a real one once I realized that he just gave me the excuse I would use for what happened to my hand. Initially I was uncomfortable about being one of the only people of my ethnicity amongst my colleagues, but the mutual motivation between everyone to further their careers comforted me. The thoughts about having to adjust were a waste of energy mentally. My mom rarely left my mind the entire day, but that only gave me a boost of energy to perform. A face to face about her being on drugs was something that I could never be all the way ready for. I went the entire workday without seeing Chauncey. I almost forgot about my eagerness to be around him until I saw him while I was rushing to my car after work. "How did today go young brother?" he asked as he approached me. "It went great." I responded. Chauncey looked at me from head to toe then said, "Ok, that's good. What happened to your hand?" I answered, "I was playing basketball and I fell on it while trying to break my fall." He smacked his mouth, then placed his hand on my shoulder and said, "What really happened? I know you weren't playing basketball." I never bought up my lack of feelings for basketball to Chauncey and he made it seem as if he knew I wasn't telling him the truth. My sense of urgency to get back home to my mother made me cut the interrogation short. "That's how I broke it believe it or not.

It was great seeing you. Catch you later boss man." I said as I walked away towards my car.

No matter how much you prepare for some situations, you will never be fully ready to face them. That still did not give me the motivation to go straight home. The gym was the only place I would usually go if I wasn't at home or school. The meds I was on made me feel like I was sitting on a cloud the entire day, so the gym was not an option. Going out to eat wasn't a choice either. Housing my mother upped my preexisting frugality. Campus was a ghost town because the semester ended. My only other option was to go by Cherry. It didn't dawn on me that Cherry was leaving to go to Miami until I turned onto her street. Her place was at the end of the block. I decided to park halfway down the block because my only other option was to head back home and I wasn't ready to deal with the situation that was waiting for me there. The spare time was perfect timing to get the ball rolling on finding help for my mother. The perfect person to call was Tanya. Tanya was my mother's best friend daughter. She showed a strong resentment towards me, but I never understood why. Her resentment probably subconsciously made me want to be an engineer so I could become a better engineer than her. Tanya was a chemical engineer for an oil and gas company named Greenwood. It was a rival company to Williams Commerce. As I searched for her unsaved number in my phone through random texts I received for the holidays, I wondered why she hadn't gotten any help for her mother's addiction yet. I knew she was pulling in over six figures a year during the past several years. Before the first minute went by in our conversation, she could already tell what happened. My anger and tears could not be disguised from hundreds of miles away. She acted as a big sister and consoled me. What I was going through was something that she repetitively dealt with. After she told me about one of the best drug rehab programs in the country, I saw my opportunity to ask her why she hadn't sent her mother there yet. Her response blew my mind.

Tanya signed a basketball scholarship to a prestigious private university coming out of high school. She chose engineering as her major at the end of her freshman year. Tanya's coach told her don't choose engineering because that major might cause her grades to drop below what she needed to remain eligible and that engineering would use up too much of her time. Tanya stayed resilient on her stance about not switching majors. During her sophomore season Tanya's coach threatened to pull her scholarship if she didn't switch her major by the end of the school year. Her coach fulfilled that threat and pulled Tanya's scholarship at the end of her sophomore year. Tanya had several full scholarship offers to continue her basketball career elsewhere, but declined them because the other colleges were less prestigious. She took several hefty loans out to stay at her school. Once Tanya began receiving student loan bills, she realized that she made a bad decision. She was finally close to being able to afford rehab for her mother.

My chair remained reclined for the two hours I spent talking to Tanya. As the sun fell I raised my driver's seat back up and ended our conversation. I knew it was time to get home ASAP. I couldn't have imagined that our conversation would have lasted that long. At the end of the block it looked like Cherry was closing the passenger's door of a red foreign car. I wanted to remain unseen, so I didn't drive up to see if that was her. Even if it was her, it was no concern of mine. I was numb on the inside. Cherry stayed in one of the worst neighborhoods in the city. It was unusual to see such a car on that block.

The sun had fallen completely by the time I merged onto the interstate. I was as ready as I could have ever been to speak with my mom. I got home in record time from the other side of town. The way I drive usually impedes the flow of traffic, but I drove like a bat out of hell to hurry home. After I parked, my heart began to pound with every step I took closer to my apartment. Only God knows what my mother did all day. I had a surprise waiting for me behind the front door. My mom had cleaned up my apartment and prepared dinner. I approached the kitchen table with a faint heart. There were a lot of questions that I was scared to know the answers to. After eating half of my meal without saying a word, my mother broke the ice. She looked at me in the eyes then asked, "Do you want to know when I began using?" I nodded my head yes without saying a word.

"Before you were born your father used to smoke weed almost every day. He handled his business after he smoked though. A lot of people smoke then disregard their responsibilities, but not your father. Your father had this friend named Phillip who was always jealous of him. Anytime your father would buy something, Phillip would buy a more expensive version of whatever your father purchased. They were friends since elementary school and reconnected once your father got him a job as a car salesman at the dealership he was working at. Phillip would come over almost every day during their first few weeks of working together. After your father got promoted to manager, Phillip stopped coming around. For six months straight he avoided coming over. Phillip showed up at our house for the first time in six months the day he got fired. I remember that day like it was yesterday because that was exactly one month before you were born. He invited your father out that night and the love of my life never returned home the same man. Phillip laced your father's blunt with some crack that night. I didn't know about that until after your father passed away on your first birthday. The guilt Phillip had from introducing your father to a drug that he overdosed on made him confess everything to me. After I gave birth to you, your father did the same thing to me that Phillip did to him. The depression of losing him only intensified my habit. I did everything I could to hide my habit from you. I always feared the day I would have to tell you this."

Throughout my life I heard over ten different stories about how my father died. I always felt it had to be something deep if his death was continuously lied about. Surprisingly I felt relieved after my mother told me the truth. That made us closer than I could have ever imagined. The truth about my father gave me peace and I was able to move forward from something that held me down my entire life. When I arrived back to work the next day I felt reborn again. I always felt it was impossible to have more motivation than what I previously had. After realizing that I was potentially one year away from being able to afford the best rehab in the country for my mother, my motivation grew to new heights. Not securing the full time position wasn't an option. It was great timing that Chauncey was on vacation for the next two weeks. For some reason I felt more comfortable when Chauncey wasn't at work. My competitive spirit kicked back in from my ball playing days once they told me that a weekly score would be calculated between Shane and myself to see which intern lands the full time job. Shane was just happy to be there. He came from wealth and had the option of working for his family business if all else failed. He was no match to be in competition with me. Shane waived the white flag at securing the full time job before the internship was over. He didn't come close to winning one competition, but I still worked as if it were him and millions of others working for the same spot I wanted.

A month had flown by and I was so caught up into the internship that I had almost forgotten that Chauncey was a part of the equation. I was reminded when we bumped into each other in the break room for the first time since we saw each other in the parking lot. "How was your vacation?" I asked Chauncey. "Miami is always great. Getting shipped overseas for work isn't. The day after I got back from Miami they sent me to Asia to tackle an assignment. How have you been making out? Has it been too much for you working here?" Chauncey replied. "It's actually a breeze. I haven't lost a weekly competition yet, and nothing has went over my head so far." I responded. Chauncey had a shocked look on his face. I did also because he asked was working here too much for me. Chauncey broke the awkward silence and said, "Wow, I'm surprised. That's excellent." I wanted to ask him what the fuck was he surprised about, but instead I asked him did he want to join me for lunch. He declined, but that was more respectful than what he did during lunch at my final interview.

I felt the need to step my game up a notch since Chauncey was sleeping on me. Later that evening I completed a project that wasn't due for another two weeks. Connor and Chauncey happened to enter my office shortly after I completed the project. When they entered Chauncey asked, "Why aren't you working on your assignment that's due in two weeks?" I proudly responded, "I finished it already." Connor broke into excitement and said, "See Chauncey, I told you he is special. He is going to be better than you one day." Chauncey defensively replied, "Yea, I would love to see that." "I bet you would." Connor responded. Both of them left out of my office after that statement. I was baffled that Connor compared me to Chauncey. Chauncey was a chemical engineer and I was a computer engineer. Our roles had nothing in common. It was similar to when a sports analyst compares a black pocket passing quarterback to a black running quarterback or two white basketball players who have nothing in common besides their ethnicity. It was a shallow and ignorant statement. I did not take it as a compliment. I was reluctantly put into competition with a higher up. There was nothing for us to compete over. He was almost a C-Level employee and I was not even a full time employee yet. There are no such things as friendly competitions in the workplace. If you think that there are, then you will become a victim to the competitor. I already felt I had a target on my back, but now the target was enlarged after Chauncey and Connor left my office.

The final two hours of my day went by so slow. I did not let Connor's ignorant statement dampen my mood. My mother and I had tickets to a comedy show later that night, so my happiness was unalterable. There was an unusual amount of traffic on the commute home. Sitting in traffic raised my anxiety about work. Going into the job I was nervous about the other intern competing for the full time position, but now I had to worry about one of the higher ups with the company. My mind was initially eased by my performance, but knowing that if you aren't in with the right people at the top, then your performance is almost irrelevant. I needed a way in with Chauncey. After giving up on traffic, I decided to take the HOV lane which I did not qualify to be in. I made it home a few minutes earlier than when I told my mother I would be back. Once I put the key in the lock, it turned too easily. It was obvious the door wasn't locked. "Mom are you ready?" I excitingly yelled. An echo was the only response I heard. I went to my room to shower once I didn't get a response because I figured she was in her bathroom getting ready. As excited as I was about the comedy show, my mind began to drift back towards work. I fixed myself a drink and finished it before I hopped in the shower. I sat on the bed after I got out the shower and was woken up three hours later by a phone call.

A collect call was waiting for me on the other side of the phone. I answered right before the incoming call turned into a missed call. After I answered the phone an operator said, "You have a collect call from, Brenda Smith. To accept this call press 5 now. To block incoming calls from this number press 9 now." Before the operator could repeat the options I pressed 5. "Mom what's going on?" I yelled through the phone. In a spaced out voice my mom responded, "Son just come get me. I was walking down the street minding my business and they said I had something on me that wasn't supposed to be on me. I don't know, just come get me baby." It was obvious that my mother was higher than the Eiffel Tower. I ran out of my place in a robe, du-rag, some P.E shorts from high school, and some house slippers. From the looks of it, I looked like I was on drugs to because of what I had on in public. The whole world could have seen me running to my car, but I wouldn't have even noticed them. I was thankful to have extra clothes in the trunk. The relief of not having to go back upstairs to change clothes was erased when I saw that the left end of my trunk was damaged. Investigating car wrecks was never a field of my expertise, but it was evident that someone hit my car on purpose. After five minutes of blindly fishing around in my trunk that was partially jammed open, I found something to wear. A note was left for me on the glass of my driver's window. It read, "Watch where the fuck you park next time and this might not happen again." It felt like I was partaking in the worst night of my life and it wasn't even halfway over with yet. The county jail was only a ten minute drive from my place. My trunk got the attention of almost everyone that was in the streets that night. Several people honked their horns to alert me about my trunk as if I hadn't seen it already. I had a friend who worked at the jail, but I was too embarrassed to ask him if he knew what happened with my mother. Her bond was a decent amount of money, so I assumed she got caught with some hard drugs. When I spotted my mother walking towards my car I got out to open the door for her. Two people who appeared to be homeless spoke to my mother as if they knew her while she was parlaying to my car. When my mom got in the car she tried to give me the same spill she gave me when I first moved her in. I wasn't going for it. I helped my mother into her room once we made it back inside. A surprise was waiting for me once we made it in her room. I pointed the remote at an empty television stand. The 60 inch television that was in the guest room was missing. When I looked at her in disgust she said, "It's not like I watch TV anyway. I figured you would rather me have the money than let me sit in front of a TV I don't watch." I dropped the remote then went to my room and cried myself to sleep.

Part 5

My misery at work the next day was more evident than the cast on my hand. Several people asked me about my mood change before lunch time. Shortly before my lunch break Chauncey welcomed himself to a seat in my office. He was in a mood that I never seen him in before. His mood was opposite of mine. "Today is great right?" Chauncey insinuated shortly after he took a seat. "It's ok, I've had better days." I responded. Chauncey smiled as if I gave him some great news and said, "Meet me at the steakhouse around the corner for lunch. My treat my man." He left before I could respond with a smile and accept his offer. After having a flat screen gone missing, a $1,000 deductible to pay, and footing the bail for my mother's freedom, a free lunch never sounded so enticing.

On the way to lunch, my mood began to change. I was finally presented the chance that I desired to establish a relationship with Chauncey. I guessed that my performance which exceeded his expectations provoked him to invite me out for lunch. Going out to eat with him seemed like a great opportunity. Before the waitress could make it to our table to take our drink orders, Chauncey pried at why I wasn't having a good day. Normally people ask personal questions because of nosiness instead of sincerely caring. Because of so I always kept walls up when people asked me personal questions. If there was ever a time to let my guard down, that felt like the perfect timing to do so. After dodging his questions, he began to reveal another side of him that I

107

didn't know existed. The Chauncey outside of work was a completely different person. He began to speak in an Afrocentric manner. He said that his job would be left undone if he didn't do what all it took to help the next generation of young brothers get to where he is. He went on and on about how excited he was about mentoring me until the waitress made it to our table to take our drink orders. When the waitress asked did I want to look at the alcohol menu, I declined. Chauncey interjected then said to the waitress, "No, bring him whatever he wants." "Can we drink then go back to work?" I asked Chauncey. He laughed as if I asked him is water wet then responded, "Of course, I do it all of the time. It's a big part of the culture at work. In fact, it helps me be more productive. Drink up man, you look down anyways. I am going to go wash my hands. Order whatever you want." If there was ever a time I needed a drink before the sun went down, that was the day. Before our entrees could be delivered I was two margaritas in. By the time I finished my lunch I vented everything that was on my mind to Chauncey. Once he took care of the tab I asked him to wait for me until I came from the restroom. Chauncey said he had to rush back to the office and leave right away. He made it to his car before I made it to the restroom door.

I reeked of tequila on the brief drive back to work so I stopped at the gas station to get some aftershave and a pack of gum to mask the smell. My anxiety of someone finding out I had drinks at lunch ruined the buzz I felt from the margaritas. I was thankful that I had no scheduled interactions with anyone for the remainder of the evening.

After an hour of sitting in my office struggling to stay awake, Chauncey came strutting in. Before I could address him he said, "Hey man I told the staff that you would be able to do a presentation of your project in about an hour. Meet us in the conference room for 3:30." My plan was to respectfully decline, but he left before I had a chance to voice my rebuttal. I couldn't have picked a less ideal time to get drunk. I knew my project in and out, but I wasn't sober enough to articulate everything. I drank two cups of black coffee and five bottles of water to sober up as much as possible. The hour I had to prepare for my presentation flew by. The idea to drink coffee paid off brilliantly. I was almost sober and fully alert. The idea to flood my body with water didn't pay off brilliantly. I stopped my presentation three times to use the restroom. I figured one employee would say something to me about having to use the restroom several times while I was presenting, but I didn't expect it to be Chauncey. "Do you need a diaper young man? What's going on?" Chauncey asked as soon as I said my last word on the presentation. Connor said, "Give him a break Chauncey. Great job. We are loving what we are seeing from you young man. Keep at it." I thanked him then left to use the restroom again before I continued onto my office for the remainder of the day.

The next day when I made it to work, it seemed as if Shane and I exchanged moods from the day before. Hanging with Chauncey outside of work put me into a great mood. Shane was mum about what was going on with him the entire morning, but he invited me to lunch during our break time. Back to back free lunches put me into an even better mood.

I spent most of that morning wondering what was bothering him so much. It was evident that it was something deep once we made it to the restaurant. He was so pressed to get a drink that he asked the hostess to put in his drink order while she was walking us to our table. My happiness for a free lunch transitioned to concern because of his desperation for a drink. I was sincerely worried about his wellbeing, so I didn't pry to see what was bothering him. After our appetizers came out, so did what happened.

Shane had to see the honor board at his university because he got caught red handed plagiarizing a paper. He paid for a paper that someone wrote in the same class a few years back and forgot to change the name on the cover page before he turned it in. I excused myself to go to the restroom because I couldn't control my laughter for a second longer. Shane ordered his third drink while I was walking back from the restroom. Before I could sit all the way down after I made it back to the table he said in a defeated voice, "I already gave up on the internship, but I did not want to get fired from it. I know that will be an automatic termination once they find out. My dad is going to be so embarrassed." "Your dad doesn't know people at this company though." I responded. "Oh yes he does. The CFO and my father are members of the same country club. They go golfing together almost every month." Shane responded. I wanted to order a drink after I found out that his dumb ass got in because of his father's affiliation with the CFO. All I could do was think about the other deserving candidates. At that point, life showed me who you know is more valuable than what you know. I had a broader vision of how cycles repeat themselves. My spite wasn't enough for me not to help him get back to work. Shane was so drunk when we left the restaurant that I had to drive him back to the office. We arrived back to work ten minutes behind schedule. His office was across from mine, so I checked on him every thirty minutes after lunch. If anyone would have stepped in his office, his cover would have been blown on sight. Water and coffee would have done him no justice. Chauncey slid into Shane's office around the same time he came into mine the previous day. He stayed much longer on his visit with Shane. It must have been his turn to present. Fifteen minutes later Shane stumbled out of his office with the bag he carried to work every day. When we made eye contact he winked at me and continued on in the direction of the elevator. Shortly after he was gone I received a text from him saying, "I told Chauncey what was up and he let me leave early for the day. Have fun at work."

My passion for how things are put together goes much further than the field of engineering. Until I started playing high school basketball, I thought my surroundings and environment was normal. The first several games of my high school basketball career were held at the school that had the highest tuition in the state. Five games were played over three days at the school, so I spent a lot of time there that weekend. I was astonished that there were no urine puddles by the urinals, no rodents in the facility, and trash decorating the campus. We beat almost every school that weekend senseless on the basketball court. The only other school that was as ran down as mine was the only other predominantly black school in my city. My school and the other black school alternated winning high school state championships in basketball, football, and track throughout my high school years. The city that I am from is not very big, so I was able to keep tabs on most of the student athletes throughout the city. The predominately white schools in the city blew us out the water academically similar to how they were blown out the water athletically. Almost every student athlete from those schools were inferior athletically, but went on to flourish economically and academically. Before harping on the finished product I began to look at the foundations of both circumstances. Sports were the main career that people from my environment saw as the best path to wealth. Most amateur student athletes chased that dream with a tunnel vision and did not bother manifesting dreams outside of that. It was not as cool to manifest dreams outside of sports at the school I went to. Sports were the nucleus of celebrated and popularized topics at my high school. A fast break dunk that I did against our rival school was talked about way more than the 34 I scored on the ACT test. Fast break dunks happen over fifty times a year on the basketball court at my high school. Only one other person in school history scored a 34 on the ACT test besides myself. I heard about almost every high flying dunker that came before me at my high school, but I had no clue who the only other person was that scored a 34 on the ACT test. The culture of the public school system does not breed success. The students at the predominantly white schools began receiving preparation for standardized testing in the ninth grade, but we weren't offered preparation until the twelfth grade. Shane was awarded the other intern spot to make $35 an hour at 21 years old based on privilege, not performance. Almost every basketball coach that coached me throughout my years of playing preached to my teammates and I that making it to the league was the way out and that's what we should work towards. Coaches preached that even harder to me because of my height, although I had already chose my career path at an extremely early age. Odds to become an engineer are much more attainable than becoming a professional athlete. Most of my teammates let the game use them, instead of them using the game. Children unconsciously chase what's glorified to them by their adult influencers. So many of the people who I played basketball with were smarter than Shane, but an unfortunate amount of them are sitting in jails, ghettos, and laying in cemeteries because they didn't have a backup plan to their sports dreams. Even for those such as myself who beat the odds, still have to go against people such as Shane for jobs in corporate America. Those thoughts made me unwind mentally. When I left the office that day I felt like I figured out one of the most important problems in this country and my spirits felt lifted that I was able to apply my professional knowledge to something purposeful outside of its field.

On the way home from work that day I received a call from Chauncey for the first time outside of work hours. "My man! What are you doing tonight?" he said in an inviting manner. "I am just taking it easy. I want to get ahead on the final project to secure the full time position." I responded.

Chauncey continued on in an inviting tone and said, "Ease up. It's Friday evening. Get out the house. You know you have the job on lock. Your drunk counterpart cannot compete with you." I was befuddled at what he was getting at. He had not invited me anywhere, but he heavily insinuated that he wanted to go somewhere with me. "Any suggestions boss man?" I asked him. "Yes, let's go on a double date." Chauncey said. I stayed silent after his suggestion. My energy was the highest it's been since I was awarded the internship. Being around my mother was a high risk to mess up my positive energy. I accepted his offer. Once I agreed he said, "It's happy hour right now at this place downtown. Meet me there in thirty minutes and the girls will get there a little after us." The thirty minutes felt like three. Chauncey and I were a mere forty years apart in age. People could have easily assumed we were grandfather and grandson.

When we sat down at the restaurant, I leaned across the table as if we had to talk in code and asked, "Does your new boo have a cute daughter or something?" Chauncey laughed uncontrollably, then said, "Look at me." Chauncey had on a pinky ring that looked fresh out of Sierra Leone, a perfectly tailored high end designer suit, and other extravagant garments. "You look like a highly eligible bachelor." I told Chauncey after I examined his entire steelo. In a braggadocios manner Chancy responded, "Exactly, shit my girl might be younger than you. These two girls are friends and love to have a good time if you know what I mean." Our table was on an outdoor patio that was near the street and front door of the restaurant. A woman who was one of the most popular bottle girls in the city walked towards the entrance. Her name was Naomi. I never met her in person but always dreamed of the day that I would. She was easily one of the best looking women in the city. I pointed her out to Chauncey and he made one of the cheesiest smiles I ever seen. "That's you?" I jokingly asked Chauncey. "Damn right, she is headed to our table." he responded. Naomi took a seat next to Chauncey without introducing herself. Once she sat down she kissed Chauncey on the lips then said, "Hey daddy." The two acted as if I was not sitting there for the next five minutes. She stroked his ego until the point where I became uncomfortable. I began to overly anticipate my date's arrival. The two did not slow down on the overly public display of affection until the waitress came to take our drink orders. The waitress asked Chauncey, "Do you want your regular to drink Mr. Rivers?" He responded, "No, let's double it up this time. Bring out two bottles of champagne please." Naomi eyes lit up after he put in the order, then she spoke to me for the first time and said, "There goes your date." My date had just entered the door by the time I looked up. Naomi excused herself to go to the bathroom after she spotted her friend. Five minutes later my heart dropped to the soles of my shoes when Cherry arrived back at the table with Naomi. Cherry picked my heart back up with her beautiful face and glowing personality. We started right back where we left off. Naomi and Chauncey were surprised at how we had such an established rapport, but we were too into each other to address it. Each couple carried on throughout the dinner as if nobody else were sitting at the table. After Chauncey took care of the tab, he slipped Naomi enough cash to cover my rent for six months. He did it so smoothly that I might have been the only person to realize the transaction.

Over the weekend Cherry repositioned herself closer to me than she had ever been. Her being there for me during the toughest time of my life made me fall for her at an accelerated rate. I slept by her place that Friday and Saturday night. I did not sleep by her Sunday night because of how late she kept me up the other nights. Having someone to miss and the feeling of falling for someone put me into the perfect mood the following Monday. I rarely bumped into Chauncey during the morning time at work, but that morning I kept running into him. I spotted him four times and avoided him each time. To say the situation was awkward would be an understatement. I knew he would ask me about Cherry. Chauncey strategically caught up with me during lunch time. He never ate lunch at the cafeteria, but I usually did. As soon as I walked through the cafeteria door, a hand on my back stopped me in my tracks. "You are a hard man to catch up with at work." Chauncey said after I turned around. "Sorry I have been hustling trying to finish strong." I responded. Chauncey smirked at me then said, "I heard you didn't get much rest this weekend tiger." then started laughing. When he said the words, "I heard" it sent me into immediate anger. After he called me tiger I laughed hysterically. He thought I was laughing with him, but he was sadly mistaken. I laughed because it seemed like my quickest way out of the situation. Once the laughs ceased, I asked him how his weekend went. He took the laugh completely off of his face then said, "She drained my pockets. I thought we were going straight back to my place after I broke her off some money, but then she dragged me to a hookah bar. She spent the whole time blowing smoke into her phone while she was taking pictures and recording herself. After we left from there she was talking about the hookah made her hungry, so I took her out to eat again. That girl must have a tapeworm. I took her out to eat ten times this past weekend. How many times did you take Cherry out?" While holding back my laugh, I responded, "Zero, we kept it inside the whole weekend." Chauncey had a confused look on his face then asked, "How much did you give her?" Without thinking I asked him, "How much what did I give her?" Before I finished my question I remembered that he gave Naomi a big grip of money at the table. Awkwardness set in, then Chauncey broke the silence and asked, "How did you get her to leave with you if you didn't give her any money?" I couldn't hold my laughter back and said, "That wasn't the first time we met. She is from my past." Chauncey's face signified disapproval. I began to feel as if I did something wrong. In a lecture like manner he said, "Men at our level have to do things differently. That's cool you know her, but you won't know her like you need to know her, if you don't play it like I'm showing you. You have to give them money in public. That's better than uploading them on social media. You are letting the world know you are taking care of her. You won't believe how much less headaches she will give you. That type of financial affection makes them feel so secure and they will give you the world after that. You won't believe what type of tricks them girls will turn if you break them off like that." Cherry already turned tricks that I didn't even know existed, but the less headaches part was something that intrigued me. Even though I didn't have disposable money, I imagined what it would be like to get approval from Chauncey and have a headache free relationship with Cherry. Maybe he was right. Cherry was perfect besides her thirst for money. I wondered how she would act if her thirst was quenched.

I spent the entire next week dodging raindrops. I efficiently avoided going on dates with Cherry, seeing Chauncey at work, and letting my mother go astray from her soberness. I was only several days away from securing the full time job. Once I got to work on the final Thursday of the internship, I came across some breaking news in my email. The award for winning the internship besides a full time job was a $5,000 signing bonus. I began counting money that hadn't been deposited into my bank account yet. I started imagining my trunk being fixed, my mother in rehab, and a flat screen in my guest room. On the contrary, I had some bad news waiting for me in my social media notifications. Cherry's birthday was that upcoming Saturday. My mind went wild about the things I assumed she would ask for as birthday gifts while I drove to her house after work. Surprisingly, the entire night went perfect. She didn't bring up her birthday or a gift one time. Because I was scheduled to be at work an hour later than normal the next day, we stayed up past midnight enjoying each other's company. I tossed and turned that night because I kept seeing Gucci purses, Louis Vuitton luggage, and jewelry floating in my dreams. After I got up to use the bathroom in the wee hours of the morning, the same dream picked up where it left off at once I went back to sleep.

I still managed to wake up behind schedule the next morning. Cherry wasn't in the bed when I first woke up. I felt guilty because I planned on making her breakfast as a sweet gesture leading up to her birthday. Before I could wipe the cold out of my eyes, Cherry appeared with a plate of breakfast for me. After she handed me my breakfast she said, "I ironed your clothes. I wanted to let you sleep a little later than normal because I know how hard you have been working to take care of your mother, and at work. Don't worry about getting me a gift for my birthday either." I don't know if she was trying to get me to propose to her, but it blew my mind that she went out of her way to make me feel special the day before her birthday. I had to get creative and make something happen for her special day.

The next day I spent my entire lunch break looking through high end stores trying to find Cherry the perfect gift. My anxiety to get her the perfect gift resulted in me not finding one at all. When I arrived back to work Chauncey was seated in my office. "Why are you back late from lunch?" Chauncey asked. I assumed he didn't know anything that happened with me and Cherry besides the weekend of the double date and I wanted to keep it a secret so I said, "Sorry, I just got caught in a little bit of traffic." In a disciplinary like voice he responded, "That's not acceptable." I started to get the notion that I was in trouble so I said, "I was trying to find Cherry a gift for her birthday." My reason caused Chauncey to remove the stern look on his face. If I hadn't known any better, Chauncey was about to write me up before I told him why I was late. "What did you buy her? I don't see any bags." Chauncey asked as if he were a member of the task force. In a defeated manner I responded, "I couldn't find anything." He walked up to me then put his hand on my shoulder and said, "This is exactly what you need to do. Take her to the same restaurant we went for the double date and sit at that same table. Go around 7 o'clock tonight when the sun is setting. After dinner is over, slide her some money then the rest will be history. Things will be how they are supposed to be after that."

I left for my date with Cherry earlier than expected because my mom acted like I was going to prom while I was getting dressed. Time was closing in on me to find her a gift. I only had an hour and a half before our date. My options boiled down to two. Either try again at the mall or stop at the bank. The bank was only a block away from the restaurant and I knew she would have loved that gift. The mall was out of the way and there was no guarantee that she would have liked the gift I picked out if I was able to find her one in time. I decided to head to the bank. I got off on Cherry's exit to get gas before the bank since it was on the way and my tank was nearing empty. I wanted to make it quick because there were more homeless people at that gas station than gas pumps. Cherry began to dominate my thoughts and made my mind drift while I pumped gas. A homeless guy interrupted my daydream and said, "Hey slim! You thinking about how much money you going to give me? Your gas stopped pumping a few seconds ago." I smiled and handed him $5 then made my way to the driver's seat. As I was about to turn out of the gas station another guy who appeared homeless tried to flag me down. When I looked at him he signaled never mind, then I looked down to put the bank's address in my GPS. After I took my foot off the brake, the same guy desperately jumped in front of my car. He mistimed his jump and missed the car completely, then started yelling, "He hit me! He hit me! Help!"

I made it to the bank several minutes before the GPS told me I would arrive. My heavy breathing did not stop until I finished my transaction at the bank. While I walked back to my car I felt relieved that I had finally done everything I needed to do before my date with Cherry and that I was only a block away from the restaurant. It was 6:00pm. I knew the hour before my date would be the only chance that I had to get some reading done over the weekend. Thirty minutes later a guy that resembled Chauncey turned onto the street of the restaurant. I watched the car for several minutes to see if it was him, but the person behind the wheel never got out of the vehicle so I started back reading until Cherry arrived. While I stood in front of the restaurant waiting on Cherry, I kept trying to see into the car that I thought Chauncey was driving. I had no luck being able to see through the limo tinted windows. Cherry had a surprise for me that I couldn't quite call a gift when she appeared across the street walking towards the restaurant. Her regular attire would normally fit like a woman trying to show off some skin for Halloween. For our date she was dressed as if she had to work the corner after we finished our meals. A blind man could tell what type of underwear and nipple rings she had on. I almost got hit by a car while rushing across the street to try to convince Cherry that we should go somewhere else. I started off on the wrong foot by trying to convince her before I said hello. She was as persistent as Chauncey that we went to the restaurant. As we walked to our table almost everyone's eyes gravitated towards her. It felt like I was at dinner with an entirely different person than the Cherry I knew. I walked with my head down while the hostess led us to the same table where we sat on the double date. I usually dominated our conversations, but her outfit left me speechless so not many words were spoken between us after we sat down. Every time the waitress would approach our table I would bite the inside of my lip because I was scared of what Cherry might order. I got by with ordering three appetizers and one large margarita for us to share. The entire time I was back and forth about following Chauncey's advice and giving her money after dinner was over. Because she went easy on my pockets at the restaurant, I was leaning towards giving her the money. Throughout the entire date I felt like someone was watching us. I checked my surroundings before I decided to hand Cherry $300 that mostly consisted of $1, $5, and $10 bills. She acted like I gave her a kidney that she desperately needed when I gave her the money. After I felt something that wasn't tangible, a car pulled off and my eyes followed the vehicle until it was out of sight. "What's wrong baby? It's like you have something else on your mind." Cherry said. "It's nothing, just the internship." I replied.

The uncertainty of the previous chain of events kept my mind boggled until it was time to wind down that night. Cherry eased my mind for the remainder of that weekend. Monday morning felt like the beginning of a new life for me. Cherry hurt my pockets and eyes that Friday night, but I finally felt like I had her where I wanted her. I was only a few days away from getting the biggest check I ever received in my life and being able to send my mom away for rehab a year earlier than what I expected. Her unexpectedly moving in with me, made me miss living alone. I couldn't wait until I officially got the news that I secured the full time position.

When I returned from lunch that day security guards were by each entrance. I went straight to Shane's office to ask him about the security guards since I made it back from lunch early. As soon as Shane opened his mouth the smell of tequila spread across the room. After it felt like I raised my head out of a bucket of margaritas I asked Shane, "Why?" "Because I don't care man. I ain't coming back here anyway. Might as well enjoy my last few days here lit." Shane responded. "I think your dad would be more embarrassed about you being drunk on the job, than how you got caught cheating on your paper. Well never mind he might not be. I can't let you go out like this though." I told Shane before I ran to my car to get him some gum and cologne to mask the smell. A random stomachache, briefly speaking to some kids that were on a field trip, and a full elevator made my trip to the car much longer than I initially expected. I made it back to my floor five minutes behind my scheduled time to make it back from lunch. Chauncey looked as if he was lecturing Shane in his office so I redirected to mine. Before I could log back into my computer Chauncey opened my door and stared at me for several seconds in disgust then asked, "Just getting back from lunch?" I quickly responded "Yes, I-" Chauncey cut me off and said, "Save it."

Chauncey's energy and vibes seemed off. I was glad that I only had a few days left to deal with it until the following year. When I arrived to work the next morning security guards were surrounding the exits again. Their presence made me regret not figuring out why they were there the day before. I couldn't wait for Shane to arrive so I could ask him why they were there. I didn't feel comfortable asking anyone else. An hour after Shane was supposed to be at work he texted me, "Yo man, I'm hungover. I'll be there in about an hour." Two more hours went by and he still hadn't made it into work yet. I usually hung with Shane during the first fifteen minute break of the day, but his absence left me with no one to hang with. The only other employees on our floor were higher ups and they rarely acknowledged us. I attempted to approach several of them during the break to ask, but their cold responses after I greeted them made me keep the question to myself. Shane finally arrived after the first fifteen minute break of the day. I was on thin ice with Chauncey, so I didn't leave my office to talk with Shane.

I spent the rest of my time before lunch looking for a nice restaurant to treat myself for securing the full time position. Right before I could close my office door and head to lunch, Connor rushed in my direction. "Lawrence we have to talk." Connor said as soon as he got close enough to whisper. "Is everything ok?" I asked. Before Connor could respond, Chauncey quickly turned onto the hallway. Once Connor saw Chauncey, he walked off as if we weren't holding a conversation. Chauncey stopped me by the threshold of my office door and said, "Hey Lawrence, hold off on going to lunch. Some of the higher ups need to see you in the boardroom before you head out." "What's going on?" I asked. Chauncey looked at me in the eyes and said "I am not sure, but I will walk you over there." Not a word was spoken on the walk to the boardroom. The vibe between Chauncey and myself was far removed from when we went on the double date. The CEO, CFO, head of HR, and Connor were seated in the same format as my final panel interview. Chauncey was the only person missing. When I sat down I gave everyone a warm gesture and it was returned with dry responses. The silence was drawn out after the dry responses. The panel looked at each other then the CEO broke the silence and said, "Performance is only one determinant of who we bring on from the internship to the full time position. Punctuality, professionalism, and how we carry ourselves outside of the workplace are all key determinants in our evaluation. Lawrence, I speak for myself and several of the other higher ups when I say that we believe you are one of the brightest interns we ever came across. The impact you have made individually and amongst others would have definitely put you on a fast track with this company. However, it has unfortunately been brought to our attention by one of our trusted colleagues that you haven't held your end of the bargain on the punctuality agreement you signed in your on boarding paperwork and terms of employment. Also several other things have been brought to our attention about you possibly coming back from lunch intoxicated and some interactions outside of work that we do not approve of at this company. Pairing the policy infraction with the other acts we deem as unprofessionalism, your termination is effective immediately."

Barrel In Corporate America Conclusion

Cherry and Chauncey never answered the phone for Lawrence again after he got fired. If the street lights weren't broken on the corner when Lawrence saw Cherry outside of the club during the summer of his freshman year, then his internship might have ended differently. Chauncey was behind the wheel of the car that Cherry got into, while Lawrence watched in the shadows across the street. Chauncey roamed the streets for several hours that night looking for a prostitute. Once he found what he was looking for in Cherry, they pulled off after he gave her $300. An undercover cop that had Cherry under surveillance pulled them over three blocks after they left from the corner she was working. Chauncey bailed Cherry out of jail a day after he was released and they maintained a relationship ever since.

Chauncey went through great lengths to make sure Lawrence did not get a position with the company. He was the only panel member that did not vote for Lawrence to be hired as an intern and Connor wasn't the only person that he tried to convince that they shouldn't hire him.

While Cherry and Chauncey were on vacation together in Miami, she went through his phone while he was sleep and found out that Chauncey knew Lawrence also. Once Chauncey caught her looking through his phone they began talking about Lawrence. Their mutual dislike for Lawrence made them devise a plan to get him fired.

Chauncey's initial plan to get Lawrence fired was to get him caught up with Cherry. He sat outside of the restaurant and took a picture of Lawrence giving her money during Cherry's birthday dinner. Human Resources did not find it grounds for termination when Chauncey presented the picture of Lawrence handing Cherry money. After that didn't work, he told Human Resources that Lawrence came back from work drunk one day, but they had no proof. Unfortunately they had proof of his three late arrivals.

Lawrence's mother overdosed several weeks after he was fired. He went several years without being able to find a job in his field. Three years after graduation, Tanya and Lawrence started an organization to help children whose parents have drug addictions.

Corporate America has been effective at masking racial progress in the corporate realm and has also been a place where the black race works against itself quite often. Many predominantly white institutes and corporations place African American faces on brochures and websites, but the depictions on the advertisements are no resemblances of reality regarding racial demographics at the places advertising them.

Privilege is one of the most disheartening effects of systematic racism. While European Americans were freely able to accumulate capital, land, and positions of power to pass down to family and around amongst other members of their race for centuries, African Americans did not have that privilege because of enslavement and oppression. On paper Lawrence and Shane appeared to be equals. Both made the same amount of money and had the same job title, but their situations differed greatly. Lawrence defied lopsided odds to obtain his position and Shane was handed the position because of his father's relationship with the decision makers. Lawrence sacrificed his situation with the company to make sure Shane was in good standing. If Lawrence would have identified the difference in his situation and Shane's situation, then he would have secured the full time job.

Formation

Hidden agendas have led Americans to believe that slavery ended in 1865. Change, specifically regarding Civil Rights, has often been misconceived as progress for the black race in the United States. The eras of Convict Leasing, Jim Crow, Desegregation, and Mass Incarceration have all recycled similar economic conditions that African Americans maintained during slavery. It is essential to understand the nuances of a capitalist economic system when analyzing the economic history and status of African Americans. In a capitalist economy, businesses will always be in dire competition for domination. The "Civil War" being fought over the unjust treatment of slaves and Abraham Lincoln being depicted as an advocate for racial equality, are two foundations of miseducation in U.S history. The "Economic War" would have been a more appropriate name than the "Civil War". These examples of swindling in scholarly texts and publications are constantly used methods of propaganda to sugarcoat slavery and distort the history of racial progress for African Americans.

The South's economy became one of the most dominant aristocracies in the world due to the profit margin of slavery. Although the North benefited from slavery, they were at a competitive disadvantage because slavery wasn't as prominent in their land. The North attempted to persuade the South to free their slaves because they claimed slavery was stifling capitalism. After the South's constant resistance,

Abraham Lincoln illegally provoked the "Civil War" to balance out the economy.

The South's economy was devastated after the "Civil War". Fields of crops were destroyed, most slaves were set free, and lost investments put the financially elite of the South into a state of disarray. Slave owners were not the only European Americans panicking. The working class and poor were also in a state of disarray. In response of the "Civil War", labor unions were formed by European Americans to maintain economic supremacy over African Americans. Scholarly texts unanimously depict slaves as field workers or non-skilled in house laborers. The array of skilled positions that enslaved African Americans held during slavery are shown accurately once every lavender moon. Some slaves held occupations that are still held in high regard in today's society. The agreements established between labor unions and employers were a highly effective strategy for European Americans to maintain racial economic supremacy after the end of the "Civil War".

During Lincoln's second presidential term, congress established the "Freedmen's Bureau" as a social welfare program for recently freed African Americans. The "Freedmen's Bureau", which crumbled shortly after its launch, was designed to provide food, housing, medical aid, and schooling. That minor win came with a major loss for African Americans, which is a repetitive narrative throughout United States history. The same year that the Freedman's Bureau act was implemented, so was Convict

Leasing. Convict Leasing was one of the most effective camouflages of slavery. A stipulation of the 13th Amendment allowed this to be possible. Enslavement was justified if it were punishment for a crime. Southern states that participated in Convict Leasing roughly averaged an annual profit of $10,000 during the 1870's. That figure skyrocketed to over $150,000 annually towards the end of the 19th century. How that number imploded is imperative to understand the structure of unjust incarceration rates of African Americans throughout history.

One method used to justify the new form of slavery was to implement new laws that focused on criminalizing and incarcerating black people. These "Black Codes", made it illegal for black people to speak loudly in front of white people, buy liquor, engage in forms of business besides farming, and not getting off the sidewalk when they see a white person coming. Another method that was highly effective and often swept under the rug when analyzing systematic racism is scientific racism. Popular scientists claimed that their findings proved that black people were intellectually and genetically inferior to white people. These findings were circulated throughout society with a political agenda to justify and camouflage slavery. Many of these same scientists are still currently praised in educational realms and scholarly texts.

The greatest era of economic advancement for African Americans was during "The Great Migration". This advancement happened because it was beneficial for the economy. At the turn of the 20th century approximately 90% of African Americans lived in the south where they were economically castrated. When "World War I" transpired, industrialized areas outside of the south faced a shortage of employees. Most of those positions were vacated by white males who fought in the war. Once demand of production increased because of the war, these companies began recruiting black people from the south. When "World War I" ended, thousands of servicemen returned to find their jobs filled by black people from the south. Financial insecurities and racial prejudices caused European Americans living in the regions affected by the "Great Migration" to attack black people in the forms of race riots and hate crimes. After the Second World War concluded, African American advancement was no longer an economic interest to the government.

Before desegregation black communities contained a plethora of black businesses, high ranked professionals, dual parent households, and gun violence was an anomaly. Black high schools had programs such as carpentry, masonry, welding, nursing, and others that prepared students to be economically independent once they graduated. One of the most fertile seeds planted for "Mass Incarceration" was the desegregation of schools. Black schools were stripped of all their programs aside from a college preparatory curriculum. That not only minimized opportunities for black people, but it funneled advancement towards other races that hadn't been economically oppressed by the United States for several centuries. Shortly after the desegregation of the schools followed deindustrialization of the economy. A countless amount of black workers were laid off or forced to accept lower paying positions. These moves stifled the African American race economically and left many in a state of vulnerability. In the midst of this structural dismantlement of the black race, drugs were pumped into the community. While black men were being stripped from their jobs and heads of households, they were repositioned in jail. A new set of "Black Codes" and a reimplementation of the Convict Leasing era sparked the Mass Incarceration era and the dismantlement of the black family. The same tactics were recycled. Political agendas were pushed through the media, laws were passed to criminalize African Americans, and other forms of systematic racism were used again. The phenomenon of single parent households simultaneously came about. Black women had a non-marital birth rate of 20% in 1960. By 1990 that percentage skyrocketed to approximately 70%. The Democratic Party taking back control of the government during the late 20th century was something that should not have been celebrated by African Americans or anyone who wanted racial equality in the United States. The Democratic Party furthered the destruction of black families and had a disastrous economic effect on the African American race. Many black voters have taken on the Democratic Party as a representation of the race. No matter which party has been in office, economic inequality, systematic racism, and racial injustices have remained intact for African Americans, while other races and minority groups have had legislation passed to advance their economic standing.

Since the United States is a corporation and black people were forced to the United States for capitalistic interest, we can view the relationship of African Americans and the United States government as a business relationship. African Americans have continued to bring the problem of racial equality to the government to be fixed for the past several centuries. No customer would bring a broken object back to the same business if they could not fix it after two or three times. During "The Great Depression" when European Americans were impoverished and unemployed at a rate significantly lower than what African Americans have historically remained, the government declared it a crisis. The government went through extensive lengths to resurrect those affected. The African American race has been under a great depression since the beginning of time in the United States, yet it was never declared a state of emergency. Throughout time, many great Civil Rights leaders have done an outstanding job at exposing propaganda. Exposing propaganda with no plan of action will only allow slavery to continuously repeat itself with a different name. The United States have fought wars over a countless amount of economic interests, however not one war was fought over the unjust treatment of black people who have shed oceans of blood to build and protect this country. The war to end racial supremacy in the United States must not be fought in physical combat. It must be fought economically and most important, unapologetically.

Power

If problems are to be discussed, solutions must be part of the discussion. The lack of power and how we react to racism presents a bigger burden to African Americans than racism itself. The word racism is often intensified and misused when speaking of its importance.

Example 1: If a student has a racist math teacher, the way that student's parents react could make the racism irrelevant or detrimental. The parents can make the racism irrelevant if they educate their child on the subject outside of the classroom and document conversations with the teacher. If a teacher has a racial prejudice towards a child, more than likely that prejudice will get in the way of teaching that student to the best of their ability. Math is a subject that is not subjective. If the answer is 2, then it won't make a difference if it's a black 2, white 2, or an Asian 2. The teacher won't have the power to sabotage the student if the student knows their work. A reason contracts and agreements are documented are to hold liable parties accountable. If parents have inquired with the teacher about their child's behavior in September, October, and November, and the teacher has told them their child has been behaving great, then in December when the teacher gives their child a D in behavior, it will be the teacher's word against theirs if the parents didn't document the conversations in the previous months. If the conversations are held through email or documented by the parents, then the teacher can be held accountable. Situations like these could have a snowball effect on the child's academic confidence and behavior if parents are neglectful. Parents can't relinquish their power to a teacher and let their children fend for themselves in the classroom or the school and the streets will end up raising their child.

Example 2: If a black business owner employs a racist person and that employee calls them a nigger, then the racism would be irrelevant. The owner has the power to terminate that employee. If a black employee was called a nigger by their boss, then the situation would differ greatly. The racist boss holds more power in this situation. A non-racist person usually reacts out of emotion when a person directs racist sentiments towards them. Emotional decisions often lack logic. What would be the most logical reaction if an employee who is supporting a family or dependent on a check from their job was called a nigger by their boss? An emotional decision could cause bills to go unpaid or their children to miss meals.

People who believe in racial equality often let their emotions get the best of them and do not realize their own power when dealing with racists. Arguing with a racist person on social media or in the streets is often a waste of time and energy. The non-racist person has given a powerless person power by letting their mood and happiness be altered by a person's ignorant thoughts that hold no value. People who broadcast their racist views on social media and publicly are typically the most irrelevant types of racists. The most powerful racists move discreetly because they need the support of non-racists to support their hidden agendas or businesses.

Education or lack thereof and incarceration are major issues that plague the black race. These problems don't originate in the school or neighborhood. They originate in the political and economic power relations between the white and black race. Power relations are guided by social and legal definitions. The groups that assign these labels authorize themselves the power to justify the way they treat those classified under those labels. When a higher power puts a label on someone, it influences how that labeled person will be perceived by others and how they perceive themselves.

Once a child is labeled a "special education student", their reputation of lacking intelligence will precede them. When someone is labeled as "wanted" by law enforcement their face is plastered on billboards, newspapers, and other forms of news publications. In result, their reputation will be altered and they will be guilty in a court of public opinion before their first court date. Even slaves have a connotation and perception with those who they preceded in life because of the power of a label.

We must ask ourselves, "What is the difference between a black petty drug dealer on the street who sells weed versus a white dispensary owner?" The best interest of the group who assigns those labels dictates the difference between the two. The government depicting one as a person of business and the other as a criminal justifies their ulterior motive to best capitalize off of both. The government will be able to collect taxes from owned property or rent, taxes from employee's paychecks, taxes from items sold, and several other forms of income from the dispensary owner. The government will not be able to collect these funds from a petty drug dealer, so the best way they can profit will be to criminalize him.

The school system is also structured to capitalize from labels. A special ed student is worth twice the amount of money to a school than a normal student. These labels are subjective and more than often a misdiagnosis. We must ask ourselves several questions: "Why was special ed created after schools were desegregated?" "If it's sincerely for reformation, why has the growth of it become incentivized?" and "Are black children born "special" at a disproportionate rate, or is it a system that influences their overrepresentation in special education?" The proportion of the black imprisonment rate mirrors the proportion of black children in special ed.

Politics, which was created shortly after capitalism, is a tool that capitalism uses to maintain control. Often time the financial aspect of politics is ignored. Politicians rarely fund their own campaign. It is essential for a politician's voice to be heard while campaigning and that can't happen without appropriate funding. Those who fund campaigns hold a significant amount of power in the market where the politician they are funding is running. Not only do they have the power of excess funds to fund a campaign, but they often acquire political power by funding politicians. Before a private prison owner became a major lobbyist for an elected president, drug dealers weren't given life sentences. After this particular president got elected, convicted drug dealers became eligible to receive life sentences plus a vast amount of laws were passed to increase incarceration and the profits of the lobbyist who contributed to his campaign. Acquiring political power by funding politicians who has the best interest of African Americans is a must for economic advancement. Simply voting a black politician in office does not equate to acquiring political power for the black race.

Along with analyzing educational, criminal, and political propaganda we must be conscious of how our education often supports a system of white supremacy. College degrees, high wage jobs, and positions in corporate America alone do not hold power. A college degree will often guarantee debt, but won't guarantee a job. More than often people who believe in racial equality help earn money for companies that oppose it and work for companies that have profited from slavery. An employee does not have the power to stop their companies' profits which they help earn from going to racist politicians, private prisons, and other forms of white supremacy. Employees can also be fired at any given moment. Entrepreneurship is a career path that must be highly encouraged throughout the black community. More black business owners will result in less black on black crime, less black people in jail, and more black people above the poverty line. The more jobs in corporate America does not mean more jobs for African Americans. Corporations are delegating job assignments to different forms of technology and foreigners. Often European Americans who are less qualified secure jobs over more qualified African Americans because of their connections with the decision makers. We must become the decision makers.

African American entrepreneurs flooding the same markets limits our reach and echoes the sentiment that we do not realize our own power. Chasing dreams is a glorified act, but we must expand our dreams. We must infiltrate other markets and become competitive in lanes where we do not compete. People who do not own businesses are also armed with a large amount of power to advance the culture economically. The generation of funds isn't a problem in the black community, but the allocations of funds are. African Americans are the only race inside of the United States that does not function as a nation. The Asians, European Americans, Jewish, Spanish, and every other racial group function as nations by recycling their dollars, jobs, bartering, and maintaining open progressive lines of communication. Aside from the benefits of oppressing the African American race, the United States became one of the largest aristocracies in the world by not having a free market economy. Other Asian and European countries have also used this practice in catapulting themselves into powerful nations. The African American race not only has a free market, but an extremely giving one. The savings rates and the amount of times that black money recycles amongst its own race are egregiously lower than every other race. Black communities are filled with businesses of other races. Majority of these businesses don't even contribute to the community or employ black people. Businesses that aren't black owned dominate the black community, yet black businesses don't dominate any community. Black consumers have left their own business owners with no market. Taking black dollars elsewhere deprives the black economic system. Other races create opportunities, jobs, and safer environments for their children and communities by recycling their dollars while the black race helps them, but abandons its own children and communities.

Often times at risk children who reach for immediate gratification such as crime, early pregnancy, or drug use are the basis of judgement, but we must realize who and what put them at risk. Children are often products of their parenting, not their environment. If parents aren't hands on with their children, their kids will become what society and white supremacy wants them to be. White supremacists are financially invested and immensely benefit from the problems of the black community, so it's against their interest to fix the problems of failing schools, incarceration, and poor health. We not only finance our own demise, but we often breed it.

Culture

An important action to empty the barrel will be to realize the true identity of the other crabs in the same barrel as them. Our conditions in society differ greatly from every other racial group. Prior to the 15th century when Pope Innocent VIII put out a public edict about enslaving Africans, there were only three ways of enslaving a person. Those three reasons were because of war, debt, or religious reasons. During that time period, Europe was impoverished and the economy was based on mercantilism. The first Europeans who infiltrated what is now the United States took heed to what the Pope said and launched the new form of slavery. With free land and free labor they also launched a new form of economics called capitalism. Black people were deprived of the fruits of their labor for several centuries, then set free penniless, homeless, and forced to practice capitalism with no capital. Radical republicans at the time stated that the proper corrective action for freed slaves were to allocate them forty acres, a mule, and $100. Andrew Johnson who replaced Abraham Lincoln saw that as an economic issue and vetoed it. From the end of slavery until the late 1960's the black civil rights movement was a powerful fight to secure systematic corrective action due to the oppression of slavery and its residual effects.

During the 1950's and 60's the movement peaked. In 1970 Richard Nixon shut down the black civil rights movement by implementing a public policy called, "Benign Neglect". "Benign Neglect" took the focus off the black civil rights movement and funneled systematic economic advancement to fabricated minority subgroups and other races. After "Benign Neglect" was implemented, zero civil rights bills strictly for black people were passed. Also, descendants of slaveholders and immigrants who weren't enslaved by the United States for hundreds of years were granted stimulus packages that black people have never received from the government. No other culture can relate to our history and status. "Benign Neglect" played a major role in stagnating the black race. Other minority groups and racial groups have continually fought for legislation to be passed to advance their economic standing, while the black race has taken a back seat on fighting for systematic advancement. Majority of the core economic standings of the black race has digressed or mirrors what it was in 1968. The current rate of black home ownership is the same as it was fifty years ago and black incarceration rates along with black unemployment rates are higher.

Two of the most important aspects of a culture are the way members interact with each other and common ideologies. Enhancing the way we see things and relate to each other can turn a powerless situation into a powerful one. A church in Mississippi demonstrated how that can happen. This specific congregation consisted of 200 members and 192 of them were on food stamps. Food stamps are usually looked at in the context of poverty, but this particular church looked at it differently and saw the power in the situation. The church members combined all of their food stamps and only spent them with a locally black owned market that set up shop in the church's auditorium. Within four months they generated enough money to buy a supermarket, 4,000 acre farm, second church, and eventually the congregation consisted of zero people that were on food stamps. Power derives from organization and relations. This congregation identified a special relationship with each other, then acted in an organized and unified manner. If these people would have acted in individualism, this group of people would have remained powerless.

A culture can't be powerful if powerless things are glorified by the culture. Purchases such as foreign cars, high end clothing, and jewelry are symbols of success and wealth in the black culture, yet they are neither in reality. The glorification of these items has influenced those who can't afford them, to either spend an illogical amount of their budget on these items or rob others of it. If things that hold true power are held in high regard amongst a culture then a standard will be set and a powerful cycle will be established. Land, credit, health, and family values must be held in a higher regard than gossip, entertainment, and items that depreciate after its purchase.

A special part of the black culture is how resilient, creative, and strong we are. Black people commonly use the word ghetto in a negative manner, but being ghetto is often a form of intelligently improvising to make it out of a situation stacked against the odds. The term was initially used amongst Europeans, but now black people have taken on the term and use it negatively to identify their own people.

Many times when black people internalize negative stereotypes made by white supremacists they unconsciously act as a racist amongst their own people.

Desegregation disarmed the culture of black businesses, black leadership, and black communities. A part of the culture that we need to revert back to is establishing trusting communities that function in unity instead of neighborhoods where there is no trust and unification. Previous to desegregation black neighborhoods had a plethora of black businesses, successful people living in the neighborhood, and trust throughout the community. Black communities are now obsolete. Now we just have hoods. Black hoods mainly consist of businesses owned by other races, the most successful person is usually an illegal entrepreneur, and there is no trust. Society has been socially engineered to think that hoods, crime, and poverty pertain to black culture. Our true culture is the opposite, that's why it's hidden in history books, media, and scholarly publications. Our culture should have fought for economic integration instead of social integration. We gave away our assets and resources therefore we hampered our opportunity to practice capitalism and gain ground economically.

The black race dominates athletics, yet it is controlled by another race. Black people account for more than 70% of the professional football and basketball players, but less than 2% of the ownership. Professional sports did not become an economic powerhouse until decades after integration. Imagine what economic position the black race would be in

146

if we manifested our own leagues instead of shutting them down to integrate leagues that didn't want us in the first place and still continue to treat us wrong. How would the economic and power structure differ if we owned our professional talents that we dominate? Collegiate athletics is an extremely lucrative business also. Integration crippled the growth of historically black colleges and enriched white universities that did not want black student athletes. Now historically black colleges are financially inferior to predominately white universities and many are close to becoming extinct because of poor funding.

During the "Jim Crow" era the black culture had extraordinary leadership. W.E.B Du Bois led the political movement, Marcus Garvey headed economics and self-love, The Black Panthers were on the forefront of self-defense, Elijah Muhammad and Malcolm X led religion, and it pains me not to list other heroic figures throughout that time period. The purpose of listing those names is to present a list of historic leaders to show that we don't have any leaders close to that after "Jim Crow". It is well documented that all of these leaders listed and many others who had a strong following that used their platform for advancement of the black culture were subject to be investigated, stalked, and focal points of attacks by the highest form of government and law enforcement. Heroes such as Marcus Garvey and Elijah Muhammad will never grace a heavily used history book for their heroic civil rights acts. Instead slave owners and liberal politicians are painted as advocates for civil rights throughout popularly used history textbooks and scholarly

147

publications. Why don't we have leaders like the ones mentioned in this paragraph? Are we scared or just not educated on what we should be fighting for?

We face a much different struggle than our ancestors. We must reimagine our own lives as if we were born into the shoes of our family members who preceded us. Could you imagine being enslaved, involuntarily sent to war, or told you can't go to certain public places because of your skin color? Our ancestors fought through those struggles so we didn't have to deal with those racist injustices. Will we fight to ensure that our kids and generations after us don't deal with the same injustices we deal with or will we just lay down and accept it?

All of the wealth in the world will do us little good if we are not healthy enough to enjoy it. African Americans have the highest mortality rate amongst all racial groups in the United States. Melanin is something that aids the health of a human being. Eating healthy is not a popular choice in the black community and often comes with harsh repetitive criticism. The American diet is something else that must be reanalyzed. If going by the European American guideline has African Americans last place in everything good and first in everything bad, then every aspect of it must be questioned. Black neighborhoods in the United States are filled with fast-food restaurants, grocery stores with depleted health sections, but are never short on liquor stores. White neighborhoods have an abundance of healthy eating options, minimal fast food restaurants, and a depletion of malt liquor options. Only an intellectually challenged person would consider this a coincidence.

Diseases are produced by political and socioeconomic factors. Lower income neighborhoods are more prone to be exposed to environmental toxins that affect health and mental wellbeing. Black people dominate the statistics of races who suffer from AIDS, high blood pressure, diabetes, and several other deadly illnesses. We must have conscious medical professionals who know how to counteract diseases that primarily plague African Americans. Having conscious educated people in the healthcare industry is still not enough. We must have systems in place where we can distribute and administer these treatments and medicines. If there is a cure for AIDS, sickle cell, or other diseases which predominantly affect the black culture and the medicine costs $5,000 a pill, what good would that do most people who need the pill?

One of the biggest areas of opportunity we have to advance economically is to work with our own homeland. Other races that have no ancestral ties with Africa have done more business with Africans than African Americans. American Jews roughly account for 2% of the United States population, but are very organized throughout the United States and maintain a strong global presence. Jewish Community Centers are a staple in almost every major city in the United States. The community centers are kept with pride, plus provide a great hub for recreation and networking. Depleted playgrounds and extracurricular activities throughout inner cities are reasons that kids are increasingly going astray during leisure time. A perfect example of how organized the Jewish are and how important they view learning their own history is that they have an organization that provides a free trip to Israel for young adults of the Jewish heritage to learn about their own culture. Most African Americans would not know who to call in Africa if they traveled to their own homeland. Asian Americans are quickly establishing themselves at the top of most educational statistics in the United States and are globally known for their educational dominance. In most Asian countries, the amount of time spent inside of classrooms and learning outside of classrooms are much higher than the averages of students in the United States. Asians have taken their economic and educational cultural practices with them to the United States. They have a plethora of corner stores, hair shops, and nail shops that don't have an employee of any other race. There is nothing wrong with any of these practices of different cultures unifying amongst their own race, yet when African Americans do, it comes with a negative connotation and they want black people to be apologetic about it. We must learn from other cultures to further our own.

Final Sentiments

One thing that all humans have in common is that everyone's subconscious thoughts are more powerful than their conscious thoughts. The subconscious is developed by information that is repetitively presented. Current day society is socially engineered by the school system, media, news, and advertisement. Regurgitating information presented by those sources has often been a measuring stick of a person's intelligence. As a person becomes conscious enough to use their mind to reanalyze the information that's been presented to them, their true intelligence and consciousness are enhanced. People that don't exercise their mind by learning more than what's presented to them will remain sleep after their eyes are open because their consciousness is not awakened.

Those who don't feel the black culture is in dire need of advancement are not conscious to reality. Black people still own less than one percent of the wealth in the United States. The black race has maintained the highest poverty rates, unemployment rates, mortality rates, imprisonment rates, and has become a permanent economic underclass. Black people account for twelve percent of the population in the United States, but own less than two percent of the businesses and over ninety percent of those businesses do not profit more than $10,000 annually. Many black people get mad at other races for not understanding their oppression, but many black people don't even understand it themselves. Some black people who have progressed economically do not identify themselves with common struggles of the black race. Regardless of how much a black person has progressed economically, they are not exempt from being racially profiled and stereotyped. No matter how much green or gold a black person has, they will not acquire white privilege. Racism is not an individual act, it is a group effort. Slave owners could not have maintained slavery without the help of others. Private prison owners could not flourish like they are without help from the government and other systems who act in white supremacy. For the black race to advance out of last place it will take a team effort.

Most of the racial injustices and violent attacks on black people that have generated heart shattering headlines have been going on prior to the recent uproar throughout society. Technology has sparked the most conscious era in history. Those who want to end racial inequality must take initiative and not depend on higher powers to end it. Momentum is high and must be taken advantage of. Progress is not guaranteed with time. There weren't many happy endings in this book because it is a similar representation to the proportion of happy endings in society for African Americans.

There is little relevance of the Willie Lynch letter being written by an actual slave owner or not. The letter purports to be a verbatim speech told by an experienced slave owner in Virginia during the year 1712 alleging that he discovered the secrets to control black slaves and to prevent the black race from unifying.

In gist, the Willie Lynch letter stated that slave owners should use fear, distrust, and envy for control of black slaves. Use every difference of the black slaves to make their race work against each other. Use the male against the female, the light skin against the dark skin, the house negro against the field negro, and whichever other differences that may exist. Make black slaves distrust each other, but make the negroes trust the slave masters and be dependent on them. Slave owners must break the African's natural string of independence to create a status of dependency. Their consciousness and culture must be stripped. Beat the black male for everyone to see. Keep the body and take the mind. In result, black women will raise black children to submit to labor and serve the masters once they become of age.

The conscious mind can easily see how that is prevalent in today's society. The most alarming part of the letter isn't that it contained effective mechanisms to control the black race and prevent the race from becoming unified. The most alarming part was that the prediction of 300 years was an underestimated value of how long these methods would keep the black race under control. If we knew our own history and concisely conceptualized our biggest obstacles, then "Crabs In A Barrel" would not be a term used to describe the black race and the barrel would have been emptied by now.

Made in the USA
Monee, IL
29 May 2020